Horizons

Health K

God's Healthy Child

Teacher's Guide

Organizer / Writer
Gene Ezell

Major Contributors
Judy Cook, Judy Bredeweg, Dennis Vander Plaats,
Anne VanderWoude, Patricia Knoester, Jesslyn DeBoer

Supervising Editor
Hazel Timmer

Executive Editor
Alan Christopherson

Design and Layout
Leann Kruger

Alpha Omega Publications, Inc. • Rock Rapids, IA

Horizons Health K Teacher's Guide

The framework for this curriculum was provided by:
CHRISTIAN SCHOOLS INTERNATIONAL
3350 East Paris Ave. SE
Grand Rapids, Michigan 49512-3054

Printed in the United States of America

ISBN 978-0-7403-1493-3

CONTENTS

ACKNOWLEDGMENTS

In the summer of 1989, a new health curriculum for Christian schools was planned. That fall a survey of teachers was conducted in grades K-6. The survey indicated that health was becoming an increasingly significant component of the elementary school curriculum. The survey also revealed that Christian school teachers were eager to have materials containing a clear biblical perspective.

Dr. Gene Ezell, a professor of health education at the University of Tennessee at Chattanooga, developed a content outline and scope and sequence for the *Horizons Health* series. He also was the first author of materials for teacher guides.

Many other individuals helped in the preparation of teacher guides for kindergarten, grade one, and grade two. The materials were reviewed and field tested in several schools during the 1990-91 academic year. Also providing input, critiques, and suggestions were Judy Cook, Judy Bredeweg, Dennis VanderPlaats, Anne VanderWoude, Patricia Knoester, and Jesslyn DeBoer.

The publications program was directed by Gordon L. Bordewyk. The supervising editor for *Horizons Health* was Hazel Timmer. Judy Bandstra oversaw production of the materials, and Cheryl Strikwerda Randall created the illustrations.

"The Church Is One Big Family" by Margaret C. McNeil from *Come Sing with Me*. Copyright © 1972 by Judson Press. Used by permission of Judson Press. (Unit 2, Lesson 5)

"God Gave Me Eyes" by Margaret L. Crain from *Nursery Songs and Rhymes* by Judson Press. (Unit 4, Lesson 2)

"Good Night, Good Night" from *Jelly Belly* by Dennis Lee. Published by Macmillan of Canada. Used by permission of the author. (Unit 5, Lesson 4)

"Hushabye My Darling" by Clyde Watson from *Catch Me & Kiss Me & Say It Again*. Copyright © 1976 by Clyde Watson. Used by permission of Philomel Books. (Unit 5, Lesson 4)

"Just Me" by Margaret Hillert who controls all rights. Used by permission. (Unit 1, Lesson 1)

"The Noise Song" by Joe Wise. Copyright © 1974 by GIA Publications Inc., Chicago, Illinois. All rights reserved. Used by permission. (Unit 4, Lesson 5)

"Parents Are People" by Carol Hall from *Free to Be . . . You and Me*. Copyright © 1974 by Free To Be Foundation, Inc. Printed by Bantam Books. Used by permission of Bantam Books. (Unit 2, Lesson 2)

"Sick Days" from *Fathers, Mothers, Sisters, Brothers: A Collection of Family Poems* by Mary Ann Hoberman, illustrated by Marylin Hafner. Text copyright © 1991 by Mary Ann Hoberman. Used by permission of Little, Brown, and Company. (Unit 7, Lesson 1)

"Somersaults" from *Rainy Rainy Saturday* by Jack Prelutsky. Copyright © 1974 by Jack Prelutsky. Reprinted by permission of Greenwillow Books, a division of William Morrow and Company, Inc.

"There's No One Exactly Like Me" by Betty Ann Ramseth and Trilby Jordan. Copyright © 1975 by Broadman Press. All rights reserved. Used by permission. (Unit 1, Lesson 1)

Role of the Christian School in Health Education

The primary responsibility for educating children belongs to parents. But in the Christian community parents do not have that responsibility alone—church and school also participate in the task of education. The church nurtures the faith of its young members, leading them to understand the implications of faith for their lives. The Christian school teaches children and young people about God's world, equipping them for lives of service. Deriving its authority to educate from the parents who send their children to the school, the Christian school supports and augments instruction provided in the home by teaching all curriculum subjects from a biblical perspective.

One curriculum subject is properly health education. Historically this subject has had low priority in curriculum planning; however, among educators today there is a growing awareness of the importance of health education in a balanced curriculum. Educators are recognizing that in order to promote the well-rounded development of children, the school must give sufficient attention to the healthful living of children as individuals and as members of families and communities. A sequential and comprehensive health education curriculum, such as the *Horizons Health* series, provides the Christian school with the opportunity to deal with basic life issues from a Christian perspective in a consistent way.

The serious health problems facing the contemporary world—the threat of AIDS, the widespread use of recreational drugs, the prevalence of teenage pregnancy, the easy access to abortion—underscore the need for a sound, Christian program of health education. More than ever before students need current, accurate information and clear direction on healthful living. Today's health crises dramatically highlight the obligation of home, church, and school to work together to bring the lordship of Christ to bear on the health education of the community's children.

General Christian Perspective

A Christian perspective on health education begins with the Bible's account of who we are and why we are here. The Bible tells us that we have been created by God in his image. We have been created male and female. We have been created to live in harmony with God, with each other, and with the rest of creation. And we have been assigned the task of caring for God's world.

The Bible has more to tell us. It tells us that because of sin our relationship with God is broken; because of sin we no longer clearly reflect God's image. We live at odds with God and with one another. We don't take care of the created world the way God intended. Even when we try our hardest, we often end up doing the evil we don't want to do (Romans 7:19). And physical death is inevitable.

But that's not the end of our story. In Christ, God has broken the cycle of sin and death. In Christ, God is making us whole. In Christ, God is restoring our relationship to him and to one another. In Christ, we are able to experience the beginning of new life—eternal life—and the hope of a new heaven and earth. We look forward to complete renewal and restoration.

It is this story of redemption history that provides the underlying perspective on health education in the Christian school. When we talk about family life, sexuality, physical fitness, death and dying, and other health topics, it is always in the context of this story.

Christian Perspective and Health Education

Christians believe that God created each human being as an organic unity. The Genesis 2 account of creation says that the Lord God formed man from the dust, breathed into him the breath of life, "and the man became a living being" (verse 7). The Bible does refer to various aspects of the person—such as the mind, flesh, soul, spirit, or heart—but the stress is on the unity of the whole being. The various aspects of a person—the intellectual, emotional, social, spiritual, and physical—are interdependent. In the New Testament the apostle Paul, writing to Corinthian Christians, supports this point of view. Some Corinthians, influenced by their pagan culture, apparently believed that gluttony, drunkenness, or promiscuous sexual activity did not affect their "spiritual" life. Paul counters by strongly denouncing this attitude (1 Corinthians 6: 12-19).

What is the significance of this Christian view of the person for education? It means that health education cannot be treated as incidental to the curriculum. Rather, it must be an integral part of the curriculum at every level. Physical fitness, nutrition, personal health, emotional health, the functioning of body systems—all strands of the health curriculum—affect the whole child. We must recognize that since healthy living affects us in our totality, health education plays a solid role in developing children and equipping them to serve God in the world.

● ●

God has given human beings the task of caring for creation. This task includes being caretakers of ourselves. The *Horizons Health* series helps students fulfill their God-given responsibility in several ways. It teaches them about proper personal and dietary health and encourages them to make good choices in these areas. For example, students learn about the different nutritional value in various foods, how family backgrounds and lifestyles influence eating patterns, and the importance of cleanliness in handling and consuming foods. The series also teaches students about personal safety, helping them to handle emergencies and to take precautions to avoid injury and harm. Another strand of *Horizons Health* deals with body systems, and students come to understand how they are "fearfully and wonderfully made." Still another strand deals with disease. In this area students learn, for example, about the defenses which God has provided for our bodies, and how each person can help prevent the spread of disease. The strand of emotional and mental health leads students to develop an honest and healthy self-image concept and to deal with feelings in wholesome ways. Finally, a curriculum strand dealing with substance use and abuse acquaints students with the risks associated with tobacco, alcohol, and drugs.

The Christian view of a person's responsibility to care for himself or herself in order to honor God runs counter to the prevailing view in North American culture. Our culture says that what we do with our body is an individual matter. Sports and fitness are often used for self-glorification, elevating the body to a higher status than it warrants. At the same time, abuse of the body through addiction, inattention to nutrition, or lack of exercise is also common. In a culture such as this, spelling out how we honor God with healthful living and nurturing Christian attitudes toward ourselves and others are crucial for the Christian community.

• •

The Christian's view of death and dying also differs from the view prevalent in society. Christians recognize disease and death as part of sin's effects on creation. Physical death is inevitable, but for those who have new life in Christ, death is not the last word. However, even though Christ has removed death's ultimate sting, death is still the Christian's enemy (1 Corinthians 15:26, 55).

One strand of the *Horizons Health* series helps students view death and dying from this Christian perspective. In ways appropriate to the developmental levels of the students, the curriculum deals honestly with topics such as fear of death, inevitability of death, and ways Christians cope with death and dying.

• •

Christians are called to reflect God's love in all their relationships. The social health strand of the health curriculum assists students to develop mature Christian attitudes towards others. They also learn interpersonal skills necessary for getting along with others. Thus students are lead to become contributing members of their communities. To answer our deepest needs, God created us to live in relationship with others.

Christians believe that marriage and family are part of a loving God's design for the human race. God, reflecting on his creation, decided that it was not good for Adam to be alone: "I will make a suitable helper for him" (Genesis 2:18). So God established marriage—and by extension, the family—as a cornerstone of creation. As part of God's creation, marriage was very good. The Bible has such a high view of marriage that it uses marriage as a symbol of the relationship of Christ and the Church.

But marriage and family have not escaped the effects of sin. Sin's results are loneliness, alienation, the breaking of family relationships, and the collapse of marriages. In North American society, these effects of sin are also clearly evident. In fact, for some, marriage and the family simply seem outdated institutions that are no longer useful. And pursuing a course of self-fulfillment is held up by many as the highest goal of life.

Christians believe that in Jesus Christ there is healing for brokenness and power to restore family relationships. He calls us to a life of service and responsibility in the family. And although our efforts are imperfect and our homes are not free of trouble, by God's grace family life can be a source of comfort and joy.

The family life strand of the *Horizons Health* series leads students to appreciate the blessings of family life and to assume responsibilities of family membership. Working through family topics—such as resolving conflicts, the importance of basing family life on God's law, knowing how sexuality affects life, and caring for sexuality in a way pleasing to God—helps students to establish basic Christian life patterns, patterns that will have a far-reaching effect on their lives.

● ●

In summary, the *Horizons Health* curriculum seeks to teach Christian students how the lordship of Christ results in healthful living. For only as students acknowledge their accountability to God and form their lives according to his Word are they able to become all their Creator wants them to become and live lives of thankfulness and service.

OVERVIEW

1. What is Horizons Health?

Horizons Health is a comprehensive health education curriculum for grades K-8. The series addresses the mental, emotional, social, and spiritual aspects of health as well as the physical. It helps students take responsibility for their health as individuals and as members of families and communities. It gives them opportunity to develop basic life skills—such as communicating, decision making, and resolving conflicts—in order to prepare them to meet the challenges of daily living. Its Christian perspective leads students to recognize that a healthy lifestyle is a lifestyle of obedience to God.

2. How is the curriculum organized?

Horizons Health is a flexible curriculum, organized into independent units. The units can be taught in any order, depending on your curriculum needs. Each unit focuses primarily on one or two main strands of the curriculum, with lesser strands integrated where appropriate. These are the eleven strands, which are addressed at each grade level:

Emotional/Mental Health	Nutrition
Social Health/Interpersonal Skills	Disease Prevention
Family Life/Human Sexuality	Safety and First Aid
Growth and Development	Substance Use and Abuse
Personal Health	Consumer Health
Community Health	

The scope and sequence chart shows the topics covered in each strand at this grade level and at the other grade levels of the series.

3. Do concepts covered in health education overlap with those covered in other content areas?

Because this is a comprehensive health program rather than a single-topic program, overlap unavoidably occurs in certain content areas. Health education, for example, teaches students about how their bodies work and how substance use and abuse, physical fitness, and nutrition can affect body structures and functions; however, structure and function of body systems may currently be taught in science. Schools may wish to integrate areas that overlap.

4. What is the personal safety component of Horizons Health?

At grades K-2 the safety unit includes a lesson on stranger education. In addition, at each level from kindergarten through grade 8 there is one lesson in the safety unit on preventing sexual abuse. In age-appropriate ways, each level deals with differentiating appropriate and inappropriate touch, developing self-protection skills, and identifying sources of help in case of abuse.

Since personal safety is a sensitive area, schools should inform parents about the content of these lessons. Clear communication not only creates trust within the community but also ensures that parents will support and reinforce personal safety concepts taught at school.

Before teaching lessons on personal safety, schools should also develop and adopt a protocol for dealing with suspected or reported abuse. Contact the provincial or state department responsible for child protective services to obtain information and copies of relevant laws. Schools interested in obtaining samples of school policy statements on child welfare that include a protocol for dealing with abuse should contact organizations like the Ontario Alliance of Christian Schools, 617 Garner Road East, Ancaster, Ontario L9G 3K9; or the Society of Christian Schools in British Columbia, 7600 Glover Road, Langley, British Columbia V2Y 1Y1.

5. What is the sex education component of Horizons Health?

Sex education is placed within the broader context of family life and human sexuality, one of the strands of the curriculum. Thus at every level *Horizons Health* deals with concepts relating to human sexuality. The grade 5 unit "Growing and Changing" deals specifically with the onset of puberty and the changes it brings.

6. Is AIDS education included in the health program?

AIDS education is integrated into the program as part of the disease prevention strand. At levels K-2 there are no AIDS-specific lessons; however, the broader health issues and concepts addressed at these levels—preventing communicable disease, the relationship between personal choices and health, and our God-given responsibility to honor and care for our body—establish the foundation for understanding AIDS-specific concepts at higher grades. At levels 3-6 students learn about AIDS and HIV in age-appropriate ways. Grade 5 material has a lesson on sexually transmitted diseases, including AIDS/HIV.

7. How can schools best implement a comprehensive health education?

Planning a strategy to implement the program is crucial for the curriculum to be effective. Three main areas to address are these: keeping parents informed and involved, assisting teachers with resources and training in specialized areas, and providing a school environment that supports the program.

First, parents need to be informed and involved. Because some topics covered in health are controversial, good communication is particularly important. Meeting with parents at the beginning of the year to discuss the content and goals of health education and sending letters home to inform parents about what students are learning and doing in *Horizons Health* (particularly in advance of lessons dealing with sensitive issues) are good basic strategies. Involving parents strengthens the program as health concepts learned at school are reinforced at home.

Second, schools need to provide teachers with resources and training. Many health education curricula have compulsory teacher-training sessions because of the special challenges a comprehensive health education program presents. Some health topics have traditionally not been part of the school curriculum in a formal way, and few teachers have had courses in health education. Thus teachers need opportunities through workshops or in-service training to become comfortable in dealing with sensitive areas such as sexual abuse and substance abuse. In addition, they need resources to support the curriculum and to keep current on health issues. Local or provincial/state agencies and volunteer agencies (for example, the American/Canadian Red Cross or American/Canadian Lung Association) are sources of valuable assistance and offer a wealth of resources. In some cases, inviting experts into the classroom may be advisable.

Third, the total school environment should support the health curriculum and reinforce classroom lessons. Students learn in the classroom about eating snacks that are nutritious and "tooth smart," but does the school ask students to take part in an annual candy sale to raise money for the school? Does the school library contain current materials about a wide variety of wellness issues? What does the climate of the school teach about interpersonal relationships, about living in community? Does the school community model what a Christian community should be? Health education cannot end when students step out of the classroom. Schools need to consider what kind of messages the total environment is sending.

USING HORIZONS HEALTH

The curriculum consists of independent units that can be taught in any order. This flexible design makes it possible for you to choose segments that meet your curriculum needs and your time schedule. The unit summaries found at the beginning of each unit give a quick overview of the unit and help you decide which units or lessons to use.

There are approximately 50 lessons at each of the K-2 levels. With a time schedule of a 30- to 40-minute session for each lesson, *Horizons Health* requires daily sessions for 12 to 14 weeks (or 17-19 weeks teaching three sessions per week and 25-27 weeks teaching two sessions per week). An interdisciplinary program, health lends itself to integration with other subjects, such as Bible, language arts, music, art, science, and social studies. Suggestions for integration are included throughout the curriculum.

Horizons Health provides a carefully planned and comprehensive framework for teaching health education. It is meant to furnish guidelines and suggestions; it is not meant to prescribe each step of each lesson. You are the one to mold and adapt the material and translate it to fit your students and your community.

Format, K-2

The units begin with an overview that includes the following components:

- A *Unit Summary* gives an "at-a-glance" list of lessons.
- *Goals* for the unit are outlined.
- The *Background* provides Christian perspective and/or helpful unit information.
- *Vocabulary* lists words students need to know to understand unit health concepts.
- *Unit Resources* offers suggestions of titles of organizations, books, kits, or audiovisuals helpful as teacher or student resources to support the unit as a whole.
- *Lesson Resources* suggests materials for specific lessons. Most of these resources are listed again in the lesson.

The lessons follow this format:
- *Preparation/Materials* lists what things are needed for the lesson and describes necessary preparations.
- *Objectives* for the lesson are outlined.
- *Background* appears in selected lessons providing specific information on health issues, alerting teachers to sensitive lesson topics, or providing Christian perspective.
- The *Lesson* offers a step-by-step outline. Each lesson ends with a suggestion for closing, providing an opportunity for reflection, self-awareness, summary, or evaluation.
- *Related Activities* presents additional suggestions for student activities, expanding or extending the lesson.

Masters for specific Teacher Visuals are located in the back of the Teacher's Guide. Student Activity pages can be found in the Student Workbook (purchased separately.)

Resources

Multimedia resources can significantly increase the impact of the health curriculum, and numerous suggestions for resources have been included. Few health education resources, however, are written from a Christian perspective. Careful screening is necessary before using resources in the classroom. In some cases, you may decide to use selected sections or perhaps to use the materials but add a critical evaluation.

The listings provide suggestions for current resources, but keep in mind that the health field changes rapidly. For example, many North American nutritionists are urging a change in dietary guidelines that redraws the chart of the four food groups and substitutes an "eating-right pyramid." So although we have included resources that are current at the time of publication, you will need to re-examine and refurbish resources to keep the curriculum up-to-date.

Many community and national volunteer health organizations offer educational materials in their special areas. These materials, which include kits, songs, filmstrips, audiocassettes, lesson plans, activities, posters, student booklets, or brochures for parents, are often available at minimal cost. Many of the materials produced by these organizations are listed in the Unit or Lesson Resources. A list of national health organizations is included at the end of the Introduction. Because new materials are constantly being produced, contacting these health organizations periodically will help you to tap an ongoing source of valuable resources.

Music

Singing together is an activity that builds community. All take part; all share in creating a delightful whole. Singing encourages togetherness, and young children usually enjoy singing and love repeating favorite songs. At the K and 1 levels particularly, *Horizons Health* includes many suggestions for piggyback songs. In addition, a few songs are included in curriculum.

Singing to God is also a natural part of curriculum in the Christian school. God's people of all ages join voices in praise and thanks to God. At the K-2 levels of *Horizons Health*, we have suggested songs that fit with some of the lessons or units. The suggestions are from the following songbooks. If you wish to obtain copies of the books, order them from your local music supplier or directly from the publisher.

Children's Hymnbook. Grand Rapids: Christian Schools International and Eerdmans, 1962.
> Order from Christian Schools International, 3350 East Paris Ave. S.E., Grand Rapids, Michigan 49512; phone 800-635-8288.

Proclaim Songbook 1 and 2. Minneapolis: Augsburg, 1981.
> Order from Augsburg Publishing Co., 426 Fifth St., Box 1209, Minneapolis, Minnesota 19103; phone 800-328-4648.

Psalter Hymnal. Grand Rapids: Christian Reformed Board of Publications, 1986.
Order from CRC Publications, 2850 Kalamazoo Ave., Grand Rapids, Michigan
49560; phone 800-333-8300.

Songs of God's Love: A Hymnal for Primary Children. St. Louis: Concordia, 1984.
Order from Concordia Publishing House, 3558 S. Jefferson Ave., St. Louis, Missouri
63118; phone 314-664-7000.

Songs to Grow on. Kansas City, Mo.: Lillenas, 1980.
Order from Lillenas Publishing Co., P.O. Box 527, Kansas City, Missouri 64141;
phone 816-931-1900.

HEALTH EDUCATION RESOURCES

American Alliance for Health, Physical Education, Recreation, and Dance (AAHPERD)
1900 Association Drive
Reston, Virginia 22091
800-321-0789; 703-476-3481

Canadian Association for Health, Physical Education and Recreation (CAHPER)
Place R. Tait McKenzie
1600 James Naismith Drive
Gloucester, Ontario K1B 5N4
613-748-5622
> AAHPERD and CAHPER are national organizations committed to promoting health and fitness through a wide variety of programs and publications.

National Clearinghouse for Alcohol and Drug Information
P.O. Box 2345
Rockville, Maryland 20847
800-729-6686
http://ncadi.samhsa.gov

National Family Partnership
2490 Coral Way, Suite 501
Miami, FL 33145
800-705-8997

Office of Disease Prevention and Health Promotion (ODPHP) National Health Information Center
P.O. Box 1133
Washington, D.C. 20012-1133
800-336-4797 or 301-565-4167
> Publishes Healthfinder, which lists health education materials (primarily for grades K-6) produced by national and professional organizations. ODPHP provides ordering addresses and prices, but does not evaluate the materials or sources.

Parents Against Drugs (PAD)
70 Maxome Avenue
Willowdale, Ontario M2M 3K1
416-225-6604
> Offers current information about drug abuse and a drug awareness workshop for educators.

PRIDE Canada
Suite 111, Thorvaldson Building
College of Pharmacy, University of Saskatchewan
Saskatoon, Saskatchewan S7N 0W0
800-667-3747

PRIDE, Inc. - United States
100 Edgewood Avenue, Suite 1002
Atlanta, Georgia 30303
800-241-7946
Parents' Resource Institute for Drug Education (PRIDE) both in Canada and in United States and Canada provides drug education resources, training sessions, and toll-free hot lines.

U.S. Department of Health and Human Services
Public Health Service
Centers for Disease Control
Center for Chronic Disease Prevention and Health Promotion
Division of Adolescent and School Health
Atlanta, Georgia 30333
404-488-5372
Offers resource suggestions and updated information about AIDS/HIV. Listed materials include audiovisuals, books and book chapters, brochures, teaching guides and curricula, instructional packages, scripts, and comic books.

SCOPE AND SEQUENCE

	Growth and Development	Disease Prevention	Substance Use/Abuse
K	• growth awareness • five senses and corresponding body parts • primary/secondary teeth	• germs and disease • preventing spread of germs • effect of smoke on lungs	• defining medicine • rule: only adults give medicine • consulting adult before using any unknown substance • choosing a smoke-free environment
1	• review of five senses • naming external body parts • joints • four main organs: brain, heart, stomach, lungs • interrelationship of body parts • growth predictions • primary/secondary teeth	• defining communicable/noncommunicable disease • preventing spread of germs • immunizations • health checkups • effect of smoking on lungs	• differentiating drugs and medicines • symbols for hazardous substances • identifying some drugs
2	• growth awareness • introduction to body systems • function and interdependence of senses • function and basic structure of eyes and ears • visual/hearing impairments	• disease symptoms • defining bacteria and viruses • how germs enter body • effects of nicotine, alcohol, and caffeine on body • identifying eye problems	• identifying common drugs: alcohol, tobacco, and caffeine • products containing caffeine • effect of caffeine on body • how nicotine enters the body • how alcohol affects physical reactions • differentiating prescription and over-the-counter drugs • reasons for using medicine
3	• overview of body systems: skin, muscular, skeletal, digestive, respiratory, circulatory, nervous, excretory (main parts and interrelationships) • growth and development problems (special populations)	• communicable and chronic diseases • AIDS transmission through blood and hypodermic needles • immunizations, proper food storage, and cleanliness as ways to control disease	• defining terms • proper use vs. misuse of substances • influence of advertising on use of over-the-counter medicines • dosages • labels for information • tolerance and addiction • harmful effects of tobacco, smoking
4	• miracle of life • hereditary factors • structure and function of blood • the immune system • hair, skin, and nails • structure and function of teeth • digestive system: parts of, process of digestion • cells/tissues/organs/systems • functions and kinds of cells	• care of skin • diseases of digestive system • lack of nutrients and disease • alcoholism • long term/short term effects of smoking • review HIV transmission through blood, needles	• review of terms: drugs, medicines, substance, prescription, OTC • side effects of medications • avoiding misuse of OTCs • harmful effects of tobacco, alcohol, marijuana, cocaine • defining alcoholism • refusal skills
5	• respiratory system • variations in growth rates • endocrine system • physical, emotional, and social changes of puberty • reproductive system	• main classes of pathogens • chain of infection • some common communicable diseases • preventing respiratory diseases • sexually transmitted diseases, including characteristics, transmission, and prevention of HIV infection	• review of terminology • demonstrating effect of smoking on lungs • refusal skills
6	• fetal development • stages of life • processes by which cells receive nutrients and oxygen: diffusion, filtration, osmosis • review of main body systems, main parts and functions • hereditary and environmental factors • impairments	• preventing cardiovascular disease • risk factors of cardiovascular disease • diseases of muscular, skeletal, and nervous systems • hereditary and environmental factors in disease • alcoholism and cirrhosis • anorexia and bulimia • AIDS/HIV	• chemical dependency and its effects • steroids • results of substance use • societal pressure to use substances • resisting alcohol advertising • strategies for resisting pressure
7/8	• characteristics of stages of life • review of interdependence of body systems • changes of puberty • review of reproductive system • impairments • identifying learning styles	• biblical view of disease • lifestyle choices and disease • eating disorders • suntanning • sexually transmitted diseases, including HIV/AIDS • review reducing risk of communicable and acquired diseases • understanding reality of health problems	• alcohol, tobacco, drug abuse (student research) • decision-making and refusal skills

	Nutrition	Emotional/Mental Health	Social Health/Interpersonal Skills
K	• food for energy and growing • plant and animal food sources • eating a variety of foods	• created unique • differences and similarities • main feelings • situations and feelings • responding to others' feelings	• minding manners • manners and feelings • listening to each other • ways to share • cooperating
1	• food and body energy • four food groups • eating from all food groups • eating healthy snacks • diet and tooth health	• created unique • alike and different • naming and exploring feelings • body language • dealing with feelings • ways to deal with anger • developing empathy	• purpose of good manners • practicing good manners • active listening steps • sharing • practicing cooperation
2	• four food groups • limiting extras • daily serving requirements • balanced eating • cleanliness and food handling • eating breakfast • smart snacks for teeth	• identifying individual gifts/interests • blessing others with our gifts • review of main feelings • identifying a variety of feelings • feelings and actions • communicating feelings • developing empathy • saying no and feelings	• communicating with others • developing social skills/manners • showing appreciation • helping others • active listening • selfish/unselfish attitudes • importance of cooperating
3	• classifying foods • combination foods • define nutrients needed for growth, maintenance, repair of body • limited nutritional value of some foods • healthy snacks • diet and tooth decay	• self-awareness and acceptance • appreciating diversity • identifying and expressing feelings • emotions and body feelings • how feelings affect thoughts and actions • dealing with specific emotions: fear, hurt, anger, being left out • humor and feelings	• developing friendships • factors that affect friendships • kinds of friendships • showing kindness toward others • laughing with, not at • active listening • resolving conflicts
4	• six major classes of nutrients: fats, carbohydrates, water, minerals, vitamins, protein • function of nutrients • serving size • lack of nutrients and disease • good food, good times	• self-knowledge and knowledge of God • being saints and sinners • individual differences as part of God's plan • using gifts to serve • how others affect self-concept • showing appreciation for others • handling and expressing feelings • avoiding self-putdowns • making decisions	• belonging to groups other than family • showing respect for others • accepting differences • communication skills • working out problems in interpersonal relationships
5	• review of main nutrients and their sources • vitamins, minerals, and their functions • function of water • individual nutrition requirements • nutrition deficiencies and health • influences on eating patterns	• growing up • identifying individual strengths • range of feelings • developing feelings vocabulary • ways of dealing with emotions • expressing feelings without blaming • overall wellness and emotions • dealing with anger in healthy ways	• wise ways in relationships (Proverbs) • forgiveness and maintaining friendships • respecting others • resolving conflicts • social skills • cooperative skills
6	• criteria for proper food selection • diet analysis • nutrients: carbohydrates, proteins, fats • reducing salt and sugar • results of unbalanced diet • eating disorders	• new life in Christ • patterns of life: inherited and acquired characteristics • handling ups and downs of feelings • interaction of feelings, thoughts, and actions • identifying and managing stress • recognizing influences • decision making and peer influence	• identifying social support network • factors that build up or break down relationships • erecting barriers: prejudice, discrimination, labeling • communication: basic elements, verbal/nonverbal, active listening • deciding to care about others
7/8	• proper nutrition and dieting	• identifying self as God's image bearer and God's child • being made new in Christ • self-talk and self-confidence • discovering, accepting, and developing gifts • using gifts to serve God/community • influence of media on self-concept • decision-making values/strategies • setting goals • developing study skills • being assertive • recognizing and expressing feelings	• biblical view of community • types of love • living in community • dealing with internal/peer pressure • using peer pressure positively • friendship • dealing with conflict • communication

	Family Life/Human Sexuality	Personal Health	Community Health
K	• families—part of God's plan • similarities/differences among families • gender differences • feelings and family • our families and God's family • dealing with death	• good health choices • dressing to stay healthy • exercise and rest • cleanliness and health • care of teeth: brushing and checkups	• health helpers • smoke in environment
1	• living things reproduce • families—part of God's plan • kinds of families • contributing to family life • family changes • death and Christian hope • Christian families in context of God's family	• making healthy choices • staying fit • eating from all food groups • tooth care: plaque, brushing, checkups, diet • grooming and health	• defining pollution • causes of air pollution • health helpers • immunizations
2	• families provide basic needs • human sexuality, a gift of God • exploring gender differences/similarities • resolving conflicts • family rules • new beginnings and forgiveness • family heritage and traditions • dealing with death	• good health habits • keeping fit and active • avoiding too much TV • getting enough sleep • eating a balanced diet • eating healthy snacks and breakfast • review of good grooming habits • tooth care: brushing, flossing, snacks	• noise pollution
3	• God's law of love as the basis of family living • depending on family members • communicating in families • living patterns and culture • life cycle and the family • sexual identity, an integral part of a person • dealing with death	• benefits of fitness • being physically fit; flexibility, endurance, strength • good posture • oral hygiene • eating healthy foods • benefits of sleep	• health agencies • role of community workers in safety
4	• institution of marriage/family • responsibility and family life • family and the wider community • communicating • death and dying	• components of personal health • building physical fitness • importance of cleanliness • posture • sleep and rest	• effect of contaminated food, water, air
5	• wellness in family relationships • family's impact on members' development • foundation of marriage • changes during puberty • authority/freedom in family life • coping with change in family life • death and dying	• concept of wellness • review of personal health practices • keeping a healthy balance • inventory of health habits • fitness and overall health • exercise and respiratory endurance	• air pollution • water pollution and health • community health resources
6	• stages of life/development • courtship, marriage intimacy • beginning of human life • fetal development and birth process • being a Christian family • societal pressures and family life • changes in adolescence and family life • death/dying	• healthy lifestyle • benefits/components of fitness • weight, strength, posture, obesity, losing healthfully • care of skin, eyes, and ears • importance of sleep/rest • oral hygiene • personal cleanliness/disease prevention • setting health goals	• community problems caused by substance abuse • treatment for alcoholism • community health resources
7/8	• family life • sexuality vs. sex • biblical view of sexuality • myths of sex and sexuality • changes in puberty • chastity and abstinence • healthy male-female relationships • sexual abuse	• healthy lifestyle choices • influence of fashion on ideas of beauty • dieting and health • physical fitness and overall wellness • review components of health fitness • review personal hygiene concepts	• community resources for getting help for substance abuse/other health problems

	Consumer Health	Safety/First Aid
K		• rules and safety • poison safety • medicine and safety • traffic safety • strangers and safety • fire safety: basic rules • emergency phoning • appropriate/inappropriate touch
1	• health checkups	• medicine safety • poison safety: basic rules and household poisons • safety and strangers • review of fire safety • car passenger safety • dealing with emergencies • appropriate/inappropriate touch
2	• aid for visual and hearing impaired	• care of eyes and ears • review of stranger education • intro. to bike safety • review of fire safety • home escape plan • seatbelts • emergency phoning • preventing sexual abuse: appropriate/inappropriate/confusing touch • good and bad secrets
3	• influence of ads on use of substances • labels as a source of information • reasons for using common health products	• risk-taking • bicycle safety • water safety • electrical appliances • preventing sexual abuse: appropriate/inappropriate touch, trickery, self-protection, sources of help • action plan for an emergency • first aid: scrapes, nosebleeds, burns, blisters
4		• accidents—emotional, decisional factors • review of basic safety rules • playground safety • bicycle safety • fire safety, flame hazards • home alone • preventing sexual abuse: definition, touch continuum, self-protection
5	• advertising and food choices	• taking responsibility for safety of self and others • basic emergency first aid • rescue breathing • preventing sexual abuse: defining sexual abuse, saying no assertively, sources of help
6	• getting correct health care	• taking responsibility for safety of self and others • safety in extreme hot or cold weather • safety and natural disasters • review of basic safety rules • home hazard check • defining/preventing sexual abuse: • self-protection, sources of help
7/8	• evaluating advertisements • media sales techniques	• review of basic safety and first aid • responding in emergencies • preventing sexual abuse • identifying and practicing self-protection skills

Unit 1

Knowing About Me and My Body

Goals

- Students will recognize that both the unique features of each person and the similarities among people are part of God's plan.
- Students will develop an awareness of their own and others' feelings.
- Students will develop a vocabulary for expressing feelings.
- Students will develop skills for appropriately dealing with the emotions.

Background

In this unit students will identify four basic emotions and become aware of the body language—posture, gestures, tone of voice, facial expression—that usually signals these emotions. They will also learn to recognize situations that may trigger these feelings and explore various ways of dealing with the feelings.

But why focus on emotions for a whole unit? What does this unit contribute to healthy living? By developing awareness of feelings and understanding more clearly what prompts certain feelings, students begin to learn how to handle and express their emotions in healthy ways and how to respond in healthy ways to the emotions of others.

What are healthy ways for Christians to deal with emotions? Mary Vander Goot in her book *Healthy Emotions: Helping Children Grow* cautions against two extremes. On one extreme are Christians who promote the idea that good children will have only "nice" feelings. Much popular Christian literature and art promote this idea by picturing only smiling, sweet children. Vander Goot warns that "if we fall into the habit of thinking that pleasant emotions are good and unpleasant emotions are bad, and if we consequently elect to cover up negative emotions rather than attend to them, learn from them, and grow from them, we lose integrity and become emotionally artificial." Showing sadness, fear, or anger is not un-Christian. However, in reaction to this "saccharin" approach, some Christians have gone to the opposite extreme, maintaining that children should have the freedom to express whatever they feel. This approach is dangerously irresponsible. For although disturbing emotions should not be stifled or denied, randomly expressing emotions with no concern for others or failing to deal with their causes is also not healthy.

To deal with emotions in a healthy way we must recognize and express the rich variety of human emotions. But we must also learn to control our emotions, to act on them responsibly. Vander Goot puts it this way: "Although our emotions are woven in with our actions, they are counselors to our actions but not their dictators. Our emotions give us a strong sense of our condition; however, we must make insightful and responsible decisions when we act to alter our condition."

To stay emotionally healthy takes maintenance. Vander Goot singles out three goals to work toward: richness, fit, and control. The first goal, richness, means being able to express a wide variety of feelings. Many people live impoverished emotional lives. Although there are many reasons for this, sometimes family and societal patterns are the cause. Some families, for example, don't allow open expressions of appreciation, affection, or fear; society frowns upon men expressing fear or sadness and upon women expressing anger. A narrow emotional life has wide implications because it keeps us from understanding the emotions of others, thus affecting our relationships with others. Fit, the second goal, has to do with how emotions connect with events. Emotions must be fitting; they must be appropriate to an event. "A pleasant feeling in the face of a horrid event is false, and despair in the presence of great possibilities is equally false," comments Vander Goot. We have a choice as to how to express our feelings. The goal is to work toward fitting emotions and fitting expressions of emotion. Control, the third goal, requires a purpose in life, something to give our lives direction. Only in the light of that purpose or commitment are we able to assess our emotional life and work toward reflecting that commitment in our emotions. The goal of control is not to stifle emotions, but to follow up on emotions "wisely so that our feelings, our relationships, our actions, and our perceptions move toward greater and greater integrity."

Christ, whose kingly rule includes our emotional life, calls us to be his disciples, to live according to the laws of the kingdom of God. By God's grace we can learn to become aware of the meaning of our feelings and to act on them in ways that lead us and our neighbors emotional health.

Vocabulary

Integrate the following suggested vocabulary:

health/healthy	happy	special	unique
sad	alike	afraid	different
angry	feelings	same	

Unit Resources

Borba, Michele and Craig. *Self-Esteem: A Classroom Affair.* Volumes 1 & 2. San Francisco: Harper, 1984 & 1985.

> Contains ideas for activities and reproducible activity sheets. Although the material is not aimed at kindergarten level, teachers may find suggestions that can be adapted.

Canfield, Jack, and Harold C. Wells. *100 Ways to Enhance Self-Concept in the Classroom: A Handbook for Teachers and Parents.* Englewood Cliffs, N. J.: Prentice-Hall, 1976.

> This classic contains suggestions for building an environment of positive support, increasing student self-awareness, and improving relationships with others.

Dixon, Dorothy. *Teaching Young Children to Care: 37 Activities for Developing Self-esteem.* Mystic, Conn.: Twenty-third Publications, 1990.

> This 77-page book is designed to promote affective education in early childhood classrooms in public, private, and parochial schools. It is divided into three sections: Awareness Sessions, Attitude Sessions, and Accomplishment Sessions.

Joosse, Wayne. *The Christian's Self-Image: Issues and Implications. Occasional Papers from Calvin College.* Grand Rapids: Calvin College, 1989.

> A critical look at the self-esteem movement.

Meagher, Laura. *Teaching Children About Global Awareness.* Lexington, N.Y.: Crossroad, 1991.

> Meagher offers valuable suggestions for promoting global awareness in children. Also included is a 13-page list of resources.

Prutzman, Priscilla, and others. *The Friendly Classroom for a Small Planet.* Philadelphia: New Society Publishers, 1988.

> This resource is put out by Children's Creative Response to Conflict, an organization with Quaker roots. It contains suggestions/activities for building community, learning to communicate, promoting self-awareness and empathy. Order from the publisher: P.O. Box 582, Santa Cruz, California 95061.

Sofield, Juliano, and Hammett. *Design for Wholeness: Dealing With Anger, Learning to Forgive, Building Self-Esteem.* Notre Dame, Ind.: Ave Maria Press, 1990.

> Written from Christian (Roman Catholic) perspective, this resource contains helpful background material for teachers.

Vander Goot, Mary. *Healthy Emotions: Helping Children Grow.* Grand Rapids: Baker, 1987.

> Written from a solid Christian perspective, this resource is "about normal emotions of normal children." The author's purpose is to help adults deal effectively with children's emotions. In Chapter 7, "Teachers and School," Vander Goot reflects on the way the school environment influences the emotional development of children.

Lesson Resources

Lesson 1

Everyone Is Special: A Coloring and Activities Book South Deerfield, Mass.: Channing L. Bete.

> For children ages 4-6, this 8 1/2" x 11" booklet gives the message that everyone deserves to be treated with kindness and respect. Order from the publisher: 200 State Road, South Deerfield, Massachusetts 01373-0200; phone 800-628-7733.

Lungs Are for Life - K. Kit. American Lung Association, 1983.

> The kit includes teacher guide, activity sheets, and an "I Am Special!" teaching poster. Although the focus of most of the material is healthy lungs, the main concept of the opening unit, All About Me, is self-awareness. Contact your local chapter of the American Lung Association to find out how to obtain the kit.

McPhail, David. *Something Special.* Boston: Little, Brown, 1988.

> In this story Sam finds out what he's good at.

Rice, Melanie and Chris. *All About Me.* New York: Doubleday, 1987.

Roe, Eileen. *All I Am.* New York: Bradbury, 1990.

> A child thinks about who he is—a child, a friend, a neighbor, an artist—and who he will be when he grows up. Intended for preschool to grade 1.

Lesson 2

Caswell, Helen. *God Makes Us Different.* Nashville: Abingdon, 1988.

Hiller, Ron and Judy Millar. *Ronno's Theme Pack #1: Self-Esteem Songs.* Kitchener, Ont.: Song Support, 1991.

> Ron Hiller is a Canadian singer/songwriter/performer who promotes positive attitudes through his songs for children. The Self-Esteem Theme Pack includes the piano/vocal score and audiocassette of four songs: "I Like Me," "I Wish I Were," "Risk it!" and "The Hooray

March!" Order from the publisher: Station C, P.O. Box 722, Kitchener, Ontario, Canada N2G 4B6; or Suite 162, 255 Great Arrow Ave., Buffalo, New York 14207-3081.

Quinsey, Mary Beth. *Why Does That Man Have Such a Big Nose?* Seattle: Parenting Press, 1986.
For children ages 3-8, this resources stresses that everyone is different and that being different is okay.

Simon, Norma. *Why Am I Different?* Niles: Ill.: Whitman, 1976.
Presents everyday situations in which children see themselves as "different."

Lessons 3-8

Aliki. *Feelings.* New York: Greenwillow, 1984.

Bourgeois, Paulette. *Franklin in the Dark.* Toronto: Kids Can Press, 1986
Reading about a turtle who's afraid of the dark and discovers that everyone is scared of something is a good way to spark a discussion of emotions.

Carle, Eric. *The Grouchy Ladybug.* New York: Harper Trophy, 1986.

Cohen, Miriam. *Jim's Dog Muffins.* New York: Greenwillow, 1984.
A book about feeling sad over the death of a pet.

Fernandes, Eugenie. *A Difficult Day.* Toronto: Kids Can Press, 1987.
Melinda's feeling grouchy until her mother's freshly-baked cookies turn things around.

Fiday, Beverly and David. *Time to Go.* New York: Harcourt, 1990.
A child sadly says goodbye to the family farm.

Friedman, Susan L., and Susan Conlin. *Let's Talk About Feelings: Ellie's Day.* Seattle: Parenting Press, 1989.
Traces the ups and downs of feelings in the day of five-year-old Ellie.

Greenfield, Eloise. *Night on the Neighborhood Street.* New York: Dial, 1991.

Gross, Alan. *Sometimes I Worry . . .* Chicago: Childrens Press, 1978.

Hayes, Sarah. *Mary, Mary.* New York: McElderry, 1990.
This story about a girl responding to a giant's loneliness ties in well with Lesson 8.

Ideas, Thoughts, and Feelings. Audiocassette. Educational Activities.
The song "Everybody Has Feelings" is a good unit song.

Kachenmeister, Cherryl. *On Monday When It Rained.* Boston: Houghton, 1989.
A boy tells about what happened each day of the week, and photographs show how he felt each day.

McPhail, David. *Emma's Pet.* New York: Dutton, 1987.

Making Faces. Filmstrip/cassette. Bowmar-Noble.
From the set How Are You Feeling Today?

Munsch, Robert. *Love You Forever.* Scarborough, Ont.: Firefly, 1986.

Murphy, Elspeth. *Sometimes I Have to Cry: Verses from the Psalms on Tears.* Weston, Ont./Elgin, Ill.: Cook, 1988.

_____. *Sometimes I Think "What If?" Psalm 46 for Children.* Weston, Ont./Elgin, Ill.: Cook, 1987.
> A child imagines a series of disasters but finds peace knowing that God is in charge and God is "right here."

Murphy, Jane. *Songs for You and Me.* LP or Audiocassette. Kimbo.
> Included in this collection are songs about various emotions and acceptable/unacceptable ways of expressing them.

Murphy, Joanne Brisson. *Feelings.* Windsor, Ont.: Black Moss Press, 1985.

Petty, Kate, and Charlotte Firmin. *Feeling Left Out.* Playground Series. Toronto/New York: Barron's, 1991.

Palmer, Hap. *Getting To Know Myself.* Audiocassette. Educational Activities.
> Several of these songs are on health topics. The song "Feelings" ties in with this unit.

Rogers, Paul and Emma. *What's Wrong, Tom?* New York: Viking Kestrel, 1989.

Simon, Norma. *I Am Not a Cry Baby.* Markham, Ont./New York: Puffin, 1989.
> It's all right to cry because often there are good reasons for crying.

Steele, Danielle. *Max Runs Away.* New York: Delacorte, 1990.

Titherington, Jeanne. *A Place for Ben.* New York: Greenwillow, 1987.

Viorst, Judith. *Alexander and the Terrible, Horrible, No Good, Very Bad Day.* New York: Macmillan, 1972.

Waber, Bernard. *Ira Says Goodbye.* Boston: Houghton, 1988.

Williams, Marcia. *Not a Worry in the World.* New York: Crown, 1990.
> A lighthearted book to help children laugh at some common worries.

LESSON 1: CREATED UNIQUE

Preparation/Materials

- Ink pad
- Art materials for self-portraits
- Optional: additional songs focusing on individual uniqueness
- Optional: Write the poem "Just Me" on chart paper. Illustrate with simple drawings (for example a father and a baby).
- Optional: Typeset "Just Me" in a large font; make copies for students.

Objectives

- Students will recognize that God creates each person as a unique individual.
- Students will celebrate and thank God for their uniqueness.
- Students will identify some of their unique features.

Background

The self-esteem movement has been the center of vigorous debate in recent years. Floods of articles, books, and films have been produced on the importance of a positive self-image and the disastrous results of a negative self-image. Wayne Joosse, in *The Christian's Self-Image: Issues and Implications*, points out that many Christians have climbed onto the self-esteem bandwagon. They see in the movement a synthesis of biblical truth and psychological health, which offers a long-overdue correction to the negative "such a worm as I" image of the self. Other Christians, however, resist self-esteem. In their view, promoting self-esteem is promoting pride and ignoring the "worm"—the sin—in each of us. They charge that the self-esteem movement exemplifies the narcissism of North American culture.

Although clearly Christians must critically evaluate the self-esteem movement, there is little question that how children see themselves is extremely important. Educators have found a direct relationship between self-esteem and success in school. And health educators have found that children with poor self-concept are more likely to take part in unhealthy and risky behaviors. Teachers are abdicating their responsibility if they ignore the importance of self-esteem. Indeed, teachers along with parents are the ones chiefly responsible for shaping self-image in young children.

This lesson provides a framework for creating a classroom in which student differences are recognized and accepted. Tell students, "God created each of you in his image. You are God's child, and God loves you just the way you are."

• •

Lesson

1. Introduce the topic of each individual's uniqueness with a few personal anecdotes. Tell students something of your unique history, likes and dislikes. Ask students to identify some of your unique physical characteristics (hair and eye color, dimples, freckles). Teach the word *unique* as new vocabulary.

2. Continue the discussion, centering on the uniqueness of each individual. Stress that God created each of us in his image and loves each of us. Paraphrase Psalm 139: 13-15. (God gave us life and knew us before we were born).

3. Teach students the lesson song "There's No One Exactly Like Me." Consider accompanying the song with motions on body movements. Other song suggestions are "Child of God" (*Proclaim Songbook 1*, 13) and "If I Were a Butterfly" (*Proclaim Songbook 1*, 14, *Songs of God's Love*, 58).

4. Share with the class the following poem by Margaret Hillert:

   Just Me
   Nobody sees what I can see,
   For back of my eyes there is only me.
   And nobody knows how my thoughts begin,
   For there's only myself inside my skin.
   Isn't it strange how everyone owns
   Just enough skin to cover his bones?
   My father's would be too big to fit—
   I'd be all wrinkled inside of it.
   And my baby brother's is much too small—
   It just wouldn't cover me up at all.
   But I feel just right in the skin I wear,
   And there's nobody like me anywhere.

   Read or recite the poem several times. If you have written the poem on a chart, use the chart as a teaching aid. Talk about the meaning of the poem together. Bring in the Christian perspective—particularly as you discuss the line "nobody knows how my thoughts begin." Lead students to understand that although friends, family, and teachers don't know our thoughts, God does. God knows us through and through. Help the class to see this as a comfort and not as a threat. God knows when we're misunderstood, when our motives are wrongly judged, and when we're mean or unkind. God knows us as we really are and still loves us.

   Students would enjoy having their own copy of the poem to take home and share with family members.

5. **Student activity.** Distribute a sheet of manila construction paper to each child. Have the children make fingerprints on the right side of the paper and draw a self-portrait on the left side. (Or, if you prefer, have students place the fingerprints across the top of the page.) Students will need help using the ink pad and making the fingerprints. Before beginning the activity, explain that each person's fingerprints are unique.

   Make a class scrapbook of the finished papers. Browse through the scrapbook with the class, emphasizing unique features of each class member. Keep the scrapbook in the book center so students can enjoy looking through it on their own.

6. **Closure:** "Today we learned that God knew each of us even before we were born, and that God made each of us special, unique. And each of us found out things that make us unique."

Related Activities

1. Plan some ongoing way to give each student special recognition. For example, on each child's birthday trace his or her body outline and draw in individual characteristics. Then cut it out and hang it in the classroom in a place of honor.

2. Have children by turns be "Student of the Week" or "Superstar." Designate a bulletin board area for this purpose. Encourage the children to bring photos of themselves, special mementoes, or art work to display. Or have the class interview the "special person" regarding family members, pets, and likes and dislikes; then record these on a large sheet of paper to display for the week.

3. Make handprints with paint or plaster of Paris. For paint handprints, provide paint in variety of colors. Students can make the print on a small paper plate (add a yarn hanger at the top). For handprints of plaster of Paris (available at craft stores), follow directions on the package for mixing. Mix only enough at one time to make about six plaques. Pour the plaster onto meat trays (one per child). Children make the print after the plaster starts to harden (remember to etch in the child's name with a sharp pointed object before the plaster dries). Consider making handprints again at the end of the year to demonstrate growth.

4. Enjoy some of the children's literature on the topic of individual uniqueness. Two suggested titles: *Something Special* by David McPhail and *All I Am* by Eileen Roe.

5. To develop global awareness, put up a poster or magazine pictures of children from all around the world with various skin tones and ways of dressing or involved in different kinds of activities. Draw the children's attention to the pictures and discuss how God made each child in the world unique and in his image.

There's No One Exactly Like Me

Trilby Jordan

Betty Ann Ramseth

LESSON 2: ALIKE AND DIFFERENT

Preparation/Materials

- Two puppets, flannelgraph figures, or other manipulatives. Suggestion: make two sock puppets. Choose socks of contrasting colors (brightly-colored or pastels); add facial/distinctive features.
- Plan and practice a puppet dialogue about similarities and differences.

Objectives

- Students will be able to recognize ways in which all people are alike and ways in which each individual is different.
- Students will recognize that God wants all people to serve, thank, and praise him.

Background

Puppetry is an ideal way to present many of the situations dealt with in health. So we are suggesting that you make two puppets to use in health. Try to create a distinctive personality for each puppet. Make them into class friends, humorous or wise commentators, or cheerful comforters. And consider using them outside of health class to resolve problems that may arise between students. Of course, if you find puppets difficult to use, you may prefer to act out the scenes yourself or rely more heavily on children's literature.

Lesson

1. Review the vocabulary word *unique*. Then introduce the idea of alike/different with the health puppets, Chris and Sal (or names of your choice). Present a short dialogue in which the puppets discuss their similarities and differences.

   Begin by telling the class, "We have two new puppet friends. Let's find out who they are." Have students ask questions of the puppets, eliciting their names, where they live, etc.

   Next have the puppets carry on a conversation:
   Chris: You know, Sal, the boys and girls want to know who we are and what we're like. I've been thinking. . . . Did you ever notice how much we're alike?
   Sal: Alike! We're not alike!
   Chris: Sure we are. Take a good look at me. See?
   Sal: No way.

   Interrupt the dialogue and have Chris ask the class to identify ways the puppets are the same (both made of socks, etc.) After class members state the similarities they have noticed, sum up their observations and add any similarities they have missed.

   Continue the dialogue:
   Sal (begrudgingly): Well, okay. You were right. We are alike in some ways.
   Chris: That's what I told you.
   Sal: In some ways, I said. We aren't exactly alike.

Break off the dialogue and have Sal ask the class to identify differences. Then finish the dialogue with Chris admitting that Sal had not been totally wrong. Summarize: "So Chris and Sal both the same and different."

2. **Circle talk.** Tell students that God has made us different from each other in specific ways. Recall that God loves each one of us the way we are. Note that all people are alike in many ways, too. Name or have students name a few similarities. Lead students to identify one basic similarity: God has made us all and wants all of us to thank and love him. If time permits, sing "There's No One Exactly Like Me" as an expression of praise and thanksgiving.

3. **Optional: Circle activity.** Stay in the circle. Ask each child to say one way he or she is the same and one way different from the child sitting to the left or right. Move around circle, giving all a chance to speak. Allow students to "pass" if they wish. If time is limited, have one child tell a similarity and the next tell a difference. Or provide a hand-held mirror to help children develop awareness of themselves and how they are alike or different.

4. **Closure:** "What did we learn today? We learned that we—and Chris and Sal—are alike in many ways. We can see ways in which we're alike, can't we? (Name ways.) But we're different from each other, too. And we can see many ways in which we're different."

• •

Related Activities

1. Read a book such as *Why Am I Different?* by Norma Simon, *Why Does That Man Have Such a Big Nose* by Mary Beth Quinsey, or *God Makes Us Different* by Helen Caswell. Then talk about how students feel about "being different."

2. Extend the lesson with a math activity. Make a graph showing how many students have green, blue, or brown eyes. Or put up a larger paper to let the children vote on a food preference such as apples or bananas, or a breakfast preference such as cereal or pancakes. Count up the tallies to see which got more votes.

3. Draw the children's attention to the poster/collage of children from around the world from optional activities, Lesson 1. Have volunteers choose a child that they like. Ask them how they feel they are the same as or different from that child.

LESSON 3: INTRODUCING FOUR FEELINGS

Preparation/Materials

- Make four posters each with the title of one of the four basic feelings and a large blank circle. Fill in the facial features (as shown below) during the class session (step 2).

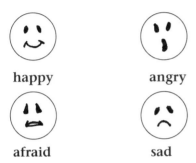

happy   angry

afraid   sad

Objectives

- Students will become aware that all people have feelings.
- Students will identify four main feelings.
- Students will recognize that feelings change frequently.

Background

Our body language sends emotional messages to others. Mary Vander Goot reminds us that we don't *have* bodies, we *are* our bodies, and "our emotions take hold of us bodily." When we look down, cover our face with our hands, or scrunch ourselves together, we are expressing an emotion—fear. And when we talk, our tone of voice can subtly communicate whether we are friendly or distant, whether we approve or disapprove. For this reason, teachers should take the time to critique their body language in the classroom. Ask yourself: Is the way I am presenting myself likely to elicit the response I wish to have from the children?

Being sensitive to body language in the classroom may also help teachers better understand individual students. For example, if a student's behavior is puzzling, observing his or her posture, facial expression, gait, or gestures may provide new insight.

Vander Goot suggests that teachers should think about ways to emotionally contact specific children. Great disparity of demeanor between the teacher and certain children may create barriers. She suggests trying to make contact through empathetic body language: "It is much easier to admit sadness to an adult whose voice, face, or posture says that this is someone who also knows what sadness is."

This last suggestion highlights one way this and subsequent lessons on feelings can serve to help children deal with their emotions. Many children believe that they are the only ones who have certain feelings. Talking about feelings and recognizing that others have the same feelings can be liberating. Vander Goot states that "one of the first steps to managing emotions is admitting to having them," and she notes that "students, who in the process of social comparison become convinced that they are the only ones who have felt the way they do, spend a good deal of their energy hiding their feelings from others and sometimes even from themselves." On the other hand, knowing that others grapple with similar emotions gives students valuable support and promotes mental and emotional health.

- -

Lesson

1. Review alike/different. Introduce the topic of feelings by pointing out another way that all people are alike: all have feelings.
2. Show the posters and read the title of each one. Then go back through the four basic

feelings one by one. Ask the children to show you with their faces what they look like when they are experiencing that emotion. Fill in the face with simple features similar to the drawings provided. Ask the children if they agree that the face shows that emotion.

3. Go through the four emotions again. For each, ask the children to volunteer to tell about a time when they have experienced that emotion. Ask whether they have the same emotion all the time. Stress that emotions change frequently.

4. **Closure:** "Today we learned that all people have feelings. And we learned that there are four main feelings. (Point to the posters and have students name the four feelings). We don't always feel the same way, do we? For example, sometimes we feel grumpy when we wake up, but after we've had a good breakfast and can go outside to play, we start feeling happy. We're going to talk about these different feelings tomorrow."

• •

Related Activities

1. Read and discuss a story that illustrates one main feeling. Suggested books: *Time to Go* by Beverly and David Fiday, *Love You Forever* by Robert Munsch, *Emma's Pet* by David McPhail, *Franklin in the Dark* by Paulette Bourgeois, *The Grouchy Ladybug* by Eric Carle, and excerpts from *Night on Neighborhood Street* by Eloise Greenfield. Have students identify the feeling and then ask whether they have ever had the same feeling. Give volunteers opportunity to tell about their experiences.

   Then relate the poster faces to the story. Ask: "Was X happy (or sad or afraid or angry) all the time in the story?" Identify other feelings of the main character during the story. Stress that feelings change frequently.

2. Make finger paintings of emotions. First ask the children to make a painting of one of the emotions. You should participate as well. When everyone has fully explored that feeling, demonstrate how feelings can change by wiping across your painting with your hand and begin to paint about another emotion. After going through all four emotions, allow the children to go back to recreate one that they will allow to dry.

LESSON 4: FEELING HAPPY AND ANGRY

Preparation/Materials
- Four feelings posters
- For making student masks:
    styrofoam meat trays, paper plates, or circles of construction paper, two per student
    tongue depressors, craft sticks, or paint mixers, two per student
    crayons or markers
    glue or tape

Objectives
- Students will recall the four main feelings.
- Students will describe various types of happy and angry feelings.
- Students will identify body language corresponding with feeling happy or angry.

Background
Happiness is a pleasant emotion, but anger is a disturbing emotion. It's so disturbing that we tend to think of it as purely negative and destructive. But anger has a positive side. Anger over unjust treatment, for example, can become a catalyst for change. Anger can move us to confront prejudice or demand justice. We know, however, that unbridled expression of anger, with no attempt at resolution, breeds more anger. And the Bible specifically warns about the destructiveness of runaway anger. We know, too, that repressed or unresolved anger simmering within can lead to actual physical illness. This lesson stresses that everyone feels angry sometimes and that it's okay to express anger. Lesson 7, which links situations with emotions, emphasizes the necessity to deal with anger in healthy and responsible ways.

• •

Lesson
1. Briefly review the four main feelings with the feelings posters.

2. Expand on the meaning of *happy* and *angry* by adding other descriptive words. (For example, "*Happy* means feeling pleased, cheerful, friendly; *angry* means feeling mad, unhappy, and sometimes unfriendly and cross.")

3. Ask: "How do we know when someone is feeling happy? How do we know when someone is feeling angry?" Dramatize these feelings and ask students to identify the tone of voice, facial features, and other body language (laughter, posture, gestures) that often reveal these feelings. Perhaps begin the exercise with an expressionless face and ask if students can tell how you are feeling.

4. **Student activity.** Have students make two masks, one expressing happy feelings and the other angry feelings. Use styrofoam meat trays, paper plates, or construction paper circles (yellow or orange for happy, red for angry). Show students how to draw simple happy/mad expressions on the masks with crayons or markers. Use the posters as models. For handles attach tongue depressors or paint mixers with glue or tape.

Extend the happy/angry faces into a language arts activity. Briefly describe a situation and have students tell how they would feel and hold up the appropriate mask:

- Someone smiles at you.
- Your brother spills juice on you.
- Someone says you do good work.
- You are invited to a birthday party.

Also use the masks during various times of the day in the classroom to have students express what they're feeling.

5. Sing "If You're Happy and You Know It, Clap Your Hands." Make up verses about being angry: "If you're angry and you know it, stamp your feet (make a frown)."

6. **Closure:** "We can often tell when people are happy or angry by looking at them and listening to them. How do they often look and sound when they are happy? (Have students hold up their happy masks and smile or laugh.) How do they often look when they are angry? (Have students hold up angry masks and scowl or stamp their feet.)

LESSON 5: FEELING AFRAID

Preparation/Materials

- Afraid student masks
- Puppets or flannelgraph figures
- Plan a puppet script about a scary incident.
- For making afraid masks:
  paper plates, styrofoam meat trays, or construction paper circles, one per student
  tongue depressors, craft sticks, or paint mixers, one per student
  crayons or markers
  glue or tape

Objectives

- Students will describe the feeling of fear.
- Students will identify body language accompanying the feeling of fear.

Background

Some people are more emotionally expressive than others. Children also differ in expressiveness, but typically they are not burdened with as many inhibitions as adults, and therefore feel freer to express their emotions. However, older children or adults who are uncomfortable with open expressions of fear or sadness, may squelch this freedom, admonishing young children not to cry ("Big boys/girls don't cry") or not to be afraid ("Scaredy cat"). In this lesson stress that when something scary happens, it's okay to be afraid, and when something sad happens (next lesson) it's fitting to cry.

Lesson

1. Put a happy mask in front of your face (or have a student hold one). Ask students to identify the feeling. What facial features express a happy feeling? Review feelings of anger in the same way with the angry mask. Then ask students to make their own faces reflecting feelings of happiness and anger. Explain that today the lesson will be about another of the four main feelings.

2. Pantomime the feeling of fear and have students guess what emotion you are acting out. Ask: "How did you know I was afraid? What did my face look like? What did I do with my hands?"

3. Use puppets or other manipulatives to tell a simple story about a scary incident that ends well. For example, pretend Chris and Sal are playing in a field near home or going on a picnic or camping trip and playing in nearby woods while the rest of family is setting up camp or frying hamburgers for supper. Briefly describe the situation and scene as you get the puppets ready. Add details and be dramatic to create a scary atmosphere.

   Dialogue starter:
   Chris: Sal, c'mon. Let's go exploring.
   Sal: Okay. (Have one tell a parent where they're going, and then have them head off in one direction together.)
   Chris: Wow! It's quiet here, isn't it?

Sal: Yeah. Kind of dark, too. Say, I'll race you to that big tree over there.

Chris: Okay. (They run, one wins, and both stop to rest.)

Sal: I've got some M & M's in my pocket. Want some?

Chris: Sure. Thanks.

Sal: What's that noise?

Chris: I didn't hear any noise?

Sal: Shhh . . . listen. Hear it now? (Both are quiet and listen and then whisper.)

Chris: Yeah . . . there's something moving in the leaves over there. What is it?

Finish the dialogue. Have Chris and Sal begin to imagine that the noise is a large scary animal and then find out the noise was made by a squirrel or bird, or perhaps by a sibling or other camper.

4. **Circle talk.** Briefly discuss the incident. Have students describe how Chris and Sal felt when they thought the noise was something scary and pantomime how they would have looked and acted if they had been in the situation. Then ask them to describe how they think Chris and Sal felt when they found out the noise wasn't something scary and to pantomime how they think Chris and Sal looked and acted. Elicit from students how their feelings changed.

5. Combine the discussion, leading students to describe the feeling of fear and how fear affects the body. Begin by describing how you feel when you are frightened. Give class members opportunity to add their ideas. Explain that the body responds to fear by becoming tense and alert in order to prepare us to take appropriate action, such as running to safety or jumping out of the way. Draw a contrast to how the body feels during a relaxed and sleepy state.

6. **Student activity.** Distribute materials and have students make a paper plate mask showing fear. As in previous lessons, use the poster as a model and show students how to draw the mouth, eyebrows, and other facial features.

7. **Closure:** "Everyone feels afraid sometimes. We can often see that people are afraid by looking at them. When we feel afraid, our bodies become ready to move fast. When we feel afraid, we can remember that God is always near and cares for us.

• •

Related Activities

1. Enjoy children's literature related to the lesson topic. One comforting book is Elspeth Murphy's *Sometimes I Think "What If?" Psalm 46 for Children. Sometimes I Worry. . .* by Alan Gross suggests ways to deal with common fears, and *Not A Worry in the World* by Marcia Williams helps children to laugh at some worries.

2. Put the puppets in a center for students to use in retelling the story of Chris and Sal and the scary noise.

3. Have students make drawings or paintings illustrating one scene of the story about Chris and Sal.

LESSON 6: FEELING SAD

Preparation/Materials
- Happy, angry, afraid masks from previous lessons
- Book about feeling sad to read aloud
- For making sad masks:
  paper plates, styrofoam trays, or construction paper circles, one per student
  tongue depressors, craft sticks, or paint mixers, one per student

crayons or markers
glue or tape

Objectives
- Students will describe the feeling of sadness.
- Students will identify body language that usually accompanies sadness.

• •

Lesson

1. Review the three feelings covered in previous lessons. Hold up each feeling mask and ask students to identify the feeling and show the appropriate body language.

2. Read a book about feeling sad to the class. Suggested titles: Elspeth Murphy's *Sometimes I Have to Cry: Verses from the Psalms on Tears, A Place for Ben* by Jeanne Titherington, *Jim's Dog Muffins* by Miriam Cohen, *Ira Says Goodbye* by Bernard Waber, or *I Am Not a Crybaby* by Norma Simon.

3. **Circle talk.** Ask students to suggest words that describe how the main character in the book felt (lonely, left out, sorry, sad, misunderstood). Why did the character feel sad? Have class members pantomime feeling sad. Talk about crying and sadness, stressing that crying is an appropriate way to express sad feelings.

   If time permits, tell about something that makes or has made you feel sad. Student volunteers may wish to share similar experiences. In discussion bring out that Jesus knows how we feel when we are sad because he felt sad sometimes.

4. **Student activity.** Distribute materials for making the last mask, a sad mask. Follow the same steps as in previous lessons. Identify the facial expression identified with sadness. Ask: "How do you think a person who felt sad would act?"

5. **Closure:** "Today we talked about feeling sad. When we feel sad, we may feel lonely, left out, sorry, or misunderstood. How do people look when they're sad? (Have students hold up sad masks.) Everyone is sad sometimes. When we are sad, we can remember that Jesus knows and cares how we feel."

• •

Related Activities

1. Center idea: make matching or sorting games with magazine pictures showing basic emotions.

2. To illustrate Jesus' compassion and empathy, discuss the Bible story of the raising of Lazarus.

LESSON 7: RELATING SITUATIONS AND FEELINGS

Preparation/Materials

- Student Activities 1 & 2
- Students' feelings masks
- Chart paper

Objectives

- Students will recognize the relationship between feelings and situations.
- Students will choose to deal with anger in healthy and responsible ways.

• •

Lesson

1. **Student activity.** Refer to Student Activities 1 and 2 in the Student Workbook. Ask class members how they think the child who dropped the popcorn feels. Then discuss the seesaw picture. Lead students to understand how situation or actions affect feelings and how different people may have different feelings about the same situation. Have students color the pictures or write the feelings on each activity sheet.

2. Play Show Me. Roleplay (or use puppets or flannelgraph figures to present) situations that elicit the feelings covered in previous lessons. Have students identify each feeling by holding up a feeling mask. Again note that not everyone will feel the same about these situations. When student responses vary, take time to explore differences.

   Suggested situations:
   Trying to tie shoestrings without success
   Eating favorite food
   Being scolded
   Going berry picking and meeting a bear
   Stubbing toe
   Playing with friends
   Being sick and missing a birthday party
   Listening to parent read a story
   Being in a bad storm
   Feeding a pet
   Breaking a new toy
   Having someone purposely take and break a toy

3. **Circle talk.** Focus on situations evoking anger and on how to deal with anger in healthy and responsible ways. Begin by referring to the last situation in step 2: "We all get angry sometimes. What can we do when we feel angry?" Brainstorm ways to deal with anger.

Include the following ideas:

- Don't do anything right away. If you don't calm down first, you may do something you'll be sorry for. Count to five or ten slowly.
- Talk with the person who made you angry. Explain how you feel and why. Then listen to what the other person has to say. Try to work out your differences.
- Do something to work off your anger (swinging on the bars, running on the playground, or looking at a favorite book).

Make a chart of the class's ideas. Use a simple drawing to illustrate each point. Display the chart in the classroom and refer to it at appropriate times.

Conclude the discussion by saying, "Everybody gets angry and that's not bad. But being angry doesn't mean that we can hurt others. Besides, there are better ways for us to deal with people who make us angry—talking to them and trying to change things."

4. **Closure:** "Things we do or things that happen to us can make us feel happy, angry, sad, or afraid. What can we do when we're angry?" (Elicit or repeat items discussed in step 3.)

• •

Related Activities

1. Show the class pictures of people in different situations and ask students to imagine what might have happened and how the people might be feeling.

2. Integrate with current Bible stories. What feelings do the characters express? Or how do students think the characters might have felt?

3. Read books about a wide variety of feelings. Ask students to identify what evoked the feeling or feelings. *Feelings* by Joanne Brisson Murphy and *Feelings* by Aliki both include a number of feelings and situations; *On Monday When It Rained* by Cherryl Kachenmeister gives students the opportunity to predict what emotion a specific situation will evoke.

4. Extend the lesson to include the main feelings. Identify and discuss other feeling words: jealous, shy, embarrassed, proud, calm.

LESSON 8: RELATING TO OTHERS' FEELINGS

Preparation/Materials
- Puppets or other manipulatives
- Plan details of the story or puppet script

Objectives
- Students will identify asking as a way to be sure of others' feelings.
- Students will empathize with those feeling left out.
- Students will originate ways to solve a problem involving feelings of loneliness/exclusion.

Background

Only as children mature both intellectually and emotionally can they begin to see a situation from another's point of view. "One way," says Mary Vander Goot, "to encourage children to take social responsibility for their own actions is to teach them to identify the consequences of their emotional expressions on others." Encouraging empathy is the best way to help students learn to be considerate of each other in the classroom. Sometimes this may involve placing students in a situation where they experience the same feelings that they inflicted on others. For example, a child who loves to tease may not understand how the victim feels until the teacher allows the victim to give the teaser a taste of teasing. "Child-centered outcomes," concludes Vander Goot, "are probably more effective than teacher-centered rules."

Use this lesson to help class members develop empathy. In the discussion, focus on how they would feel if they were in a similar situation and how they would like to be treated.

• •

Lesson

1. Ask: "How do we know how others are feeling? Often we can tell by how people look or act but not always. Sometimes we have to ask. If Bertie is unusually quiet, he may be tired, but he may be sad or upset about something."

2. Use a puppet to act out a scene in which Sal is alone and wanting to play with someone.

   Dialogue starter:
   Teacher: What's the matter, Sal?
   Sal (sighing): Oh, nothing.
   Teacher: Nothing? What are you doing?
   Sal: Oh, nothing. I came out to play with Chris and Jamie, but they're playing a game together. They say that only two can play. So . . .
   Continue the dialogue, developing the idea of Sal's hurt feelings about being excluded.

   As an alternative teaching strategy, use the dialogue ideas to tell a simple story of Sal and his hurt feelings.

3. **Discussion.** Interrupt the puppet skit or story to ask students to describe how Sal feels and why (or have students ask Sal and let her reply). "If you were Chris or Jamie, how could you make Sal feel better?" Encourage class members to think of several ways to solve the problem situation. (For example, Sal can find someone else to play with or find something to do by herself; Chris and Jamie can play a different game that includes Sal, or they can tell her that after they finish their game they'll play with her.)

Talk about the meaning of God's commandment to love others as ourselves. Relate the commandment to the lesson story, leading students to understand that being concerned about how others are feeling is one way to obey God's command.

Have students decide which of the suggested solutions is the best.

4. Conclude the puppet skit or story using the solution chosen by the students.

5. **Closure:** "How can we tell how others feel? (By looking, listening, and asking.) When we love other people, we care about how they feel. By helping Chris and Jamie decide how to make Sal feel better, we learned ways we can show other people we care about them."

● ●

Related Activities

1. Try making a cooperative monster to encourage imaginative expression and reinforce unit concepts about feelings. Students can construct a large creature from cardboard boxes and decide on its characteristics. Is it angry, happy, sad, or afraid? Why? What can the class do to make it feel better? Integrate the activity with language arts and art by making up a class story about the creature and drawing story illustrations. Consider asking each student to illustrate part of the story and make a large class book. Use the completed book to review unit concepts.

2. Center idea: students can use puppets to retell the story of Sal, Chris, and Jamie.

3. Ask children to dictate a chart story about another situation in which a person is feeling left out or hurt. Have them use their hand masks to retell the story.

4. Sing songs on the theme of loving one another. Two suggested titles (different songs): "Love One Another" (*Proclaim Songbook 1*, 37), "Love One Another" (*Songs of God's Love,* 64).

Unit 2

Living in a Family

Goals

- Students will become aware of the relationships of their families to God's family.
- Students will become aware of their role in the family.
- Students will develop an understanding of family life—its structures, responsibilities, joys, and sorrows.

Background

God created us to live in relationship with others. Genesis 2 gives us pictures of the Creator God thinking over Adam's relationships and deciding that Adam needed another human being with whom to share his life. "It is not good for the man to be alone. I will make a helper suitable for him" (verse 18). Marriage and, by extension, the family are part of a loving God's plan for human life. The Scriptures affirm this throughout (see, for example, Psalm 127: 3-4). The idea that marriage is a good gift is highlighted by the frequent use in Scripture of marriage as a metaphor of God's relationship to his people (Hosea 1-4, Isaiah 54:4-6, Mark 2:19-20; Ephesians 5:22-33, Revelation 19:7-9).

But marriage and family life have not escaped the effects of sin. Because we are sinful, we have no power within ourselves to maintain healthy family relationships. Our brokenness is reflected in family life. But in Christ we can find healing, forgiveness, and the power to restore relationships and make new beginnings.

With this Christian perspective in mind, how do we teach a unit on the family? As Christians we want to celebrate the joy of God's good gift of family, but we also must recognize the existence of common family struggles. Our homes are not trouble free, and glossing over the effects of sin is not helpful to our students. The Bible is brutally honest in its picture of family life. Think of the stories about the families of Isaac, Jacob, David, and Solomon. Teaching the unit in a moralistic way will only serve to make students who live in troubled families feel guilty. God is present in both troubled and tranquil families. The good news is that God comes to sinners, to all those with broken and contrite hearts.

Vocabulary

Integrate the following suggested vocabulary:

family	church	girl	people
body	forgive	mother	father
parent(s)	big	plan	boy

names of body parts:

penis	breast	vulva	navel
buttocks			

Unit Resources

Anderson, Ray S., and Dennis B. Guernsey. *On Being Family: A Social Theology of the Family.* Grand Rapids: Eerdmans, 1985.
> Written by two Fuller Seminary professors, the central thesis of this teacher resource is that "God has placed human persons in a created order for which the covenant love of God provides the fundamental paradigm" for the formation of family life.

Hart, Carole, and others, eds. *Free to Be . . . You and Me.* Toronto/New York: Bantam, 1972.
> A collection of poems, stories, and songs that attempt to break down stereotypes and promote self-esteem. One poem from this source is included in Lesson 2 of this unit.

Hoberman, Mary Ann. *Fathers, Mothers, Sisters, Brothers: A Collection of Family Poems.* Boston: Little, Brown, 1991.
> Written from a child's point of view, this collection includes poems about grandparents, cousins, family outings, and being an only child. Some are too advanced for kindergarten level.

Kostelnik, Marjorie J., and others. *Teaching Young Children Using Themes.* Glenview, Ill.: Scott Foresman, Good Year Books, 1991.

Lesson Resources

Lesson 1

Borack, Barbara. *Grandpa.* New York: Harper, 1967.

Brown, Margaret W. *The Runaway Bunny.* New York: Harper Collins, 1977.
> In this classic about an imaginary game of hide-and-seek, a young bunny keeps running away from his mother who lovingly finds him every time. Available with a read-along cassette from KIMBO.

Dantzer-Rosenthal, Marya. *Some Things Are Different, Some Things Are the Same.* Niles, Ill., Whitman, 1986.
> Compares the homes and families of two friends.

Joosse, Barbara M. *Mama, Do You Love Me?* San Francisco: Chronicle Books, 1991.
> "Mama, do you love me? asks a child, and the mother reassures the child of her unconditional love. Set in the Arctic, this story also introduces readers to traditional Inuit culture.

McPhail, David. *Sisters.* New York: Harcourt, 1984.

Martin, Boynton. *Why Do You Love Me?* New York: Greenwillow, 1988.
    While a father and son are taking a walk, the son questions his father about love.

Skorpen, Liesel. *Mandy's Grandmother.* New York: Dial Books, 1975.

Vendrell, Carme, and J.M. Parramón. *Family: Parents.* Educational Series. Toronto/New York: Barron's, 1987.
    About the role of parents in raising and caring for children and about how the feelings of a child can affect a parent.

_____. *Family: Grandparents.* Educational Series. Toronto/New York: Barron's, 1987.
    About the place of grandparents in the family.

Lesson 2

Andry, Andrew, and Steven Schepp. *How Babies are Made.* Boston: Little, Brown, 1984.
    Introduction to basic facts of sexuality for preschool and up.

Greene, Carol. *Why Boys and Girls Are Different.* Learning About Sex Series. St. Louis: Concordia, 1982.
    Written from a solid Christian perspective for ages 3-5, the book is about differences between boys and girls (uses the words *vagina* and *penis*). But it also looks at other topics covered in the unit: different kinds of families and the Christian family as part of God's family. This series is also available on videocassette. An excellent resource for this unit. One criticism: the art gives the impression of embarrassment with the subject (everyone has large eyes and sheepish expressions).

Henkes, Kevin. *Chester's Way.* New York: Greenwillow, 1988.

Merriam, Eve. *Boys & Girls, Girls & Boys.* New York: Holt, 1972.

Rice, Melanie and Chris. *All About Things People Do.* New York: Doubleday, 1990.

Vendrell, Carme, and J.M. Parramón. *Family: Children.* Educational Series. Toronto/New York: Barron's, 1985.
    Included are concepts of similarities and differences between boys and girls.

Waxman, Stephanie. *What Is a Girl? What Is a Boy?* New York: Crowell, 1976, 1989.
    Intended for ages 3-7, this resource teaches children about gender differences in a non-threatening way. Included are photographs of babies showing genitals.

Zolotow, Charlotte. *William's Doll.* New York: Harper, 1972.
    This classic is about a boy who wants a doll. For a musical setting by Mary Rodgers see the book *Free to Be . . . You and Me. William's Doll* is also available on videocassette.

Lesson 4

Berenstain, Stan and Jan. *The Berenstain Bears Get in a Fight.* New York: Random, 1982.
    Several titles in the Berenstain Bears Series deal with health topics. One criticism: the series tends to picture the father as bumbling and incompetent.

Brandenberg, Fritz. *It's Not My Fault.* New York: Greenwillow, 1980.

Hoban, Russell. *A Baby Sister for Frances.* New York: Harper, 1964.

Keller, Holly. *Maxine in the Middle.* New York: Greenwillow, 1989.

Zolotow, Charlotte. *If It Weren't for You.* New York: Harper, 1966.

_____ __. *Timothy Too.* Boston: Houghton, 1986.

Lesson 6

Kopp Ruth. *Where Has Grandpa Gone?* Grand Rapids: Zondervan, 1983.
    Written from a Christian perspective, this teacher resource describes how a child perceives death at various age levels and gives suggestions for guiding children through times of loss. Includes a read-aloud section to help explain the meaning of death to children.

The following is a list of K-2 student resources.

Books about the death of pets

Brown, Margaret Wise. *The Dead Bird.* Reading, Mass.: Addison-Wesley, 1938 & 1965.

Cohen, Miriam. *Jim's Dog Muffins.* New York: Greenwillow, 1984.

Keller, Holly. *Goodbye, Max.* New York: Greenwillow, 1984.

Sanford, Doris. *It Must Hurt a Lot: A Child's Book About Death.* Portland, Ore.: Multnomah, 1986.

Stock, Catherine. *Better With Two.* New York: Harper, 1988.

Wahl, Mats. *Grandfather's Laika.* Minneapolis: Carolrhoda Books, 1990

Books dealing with moving and change or loss

Aliki. *We Are Best Friends.* New York: Greenwillow, 1982.

Hickman, Martha. *My Friend William Moved Away.* Nashville: Abingdon, 1979.

Hughes, Shirley. *Moving Molly.* New York: Lothrop, 1988.

Sharmat, Marjorie. *Mitchell Is Moving.* Rainbow Reading Book. New York: Macmillan, 1978.

Waber, Bernard. *Ira Says Goodbye.* Boston: Houghton, 1988.

Zolotow, Charlotte. *Janey.* New York: Harper, 1973.

Books dealing with human death

Clifton, Lucille. *Everett Anderson's Goodbye.* New York: Holt, 1983.
    Everett grieves for his dead father. The book begins with a list of the five stages of grieving and then follows Everett through each stage of grief.

Egger, Bettina. *Marianne's Grandmother.* New York: Dutton, 1987.

Gould, Deborah. *Grandpa's Slide Show.* New York: Lothrop, 1987.

Kaldhol, Marit, and Wenche Oyen. *Goodbye Rune.* New York: Kane/Miller, 1987.

Cohn, Janice. *I Had a Friend Named Peter: Talking to Children About Death.* New York: Morrow, 1987.

LESSON 1: A FAMILY IS…

Preparation/Materials
- Pictures of different types of families. Include a wide variety of families: a couple with no children, a family with one child, a large family, and a single-parent family; African-American, Hispanic, Asian and Caucasian families; families from around the world.

Objectives
- Students will identify the concept of family.
- Students will recognize that families are part of God's plan.
- Students will identify ways in which families are alike and different.

Background
"God established marriage and, by extension, the family as a cornerstone of creation," says this curriculum's statement of philosophy. In this lesson, lead students to understand that the family is part of God's loving design for the human race and awaken in them an appreciation of the blessings of family life.

• •

Lesson

1. Ask children if they live alone. Elicit responses about whom they live with. Explain that God made us in such a way that we like and need to live with others. And God puts each of us in a special family. God's plan for people includes living in families, living with others. Ask: "Why do you think God created us to live in families?" Lead students to appreciate God's loving design in making families whose members love each other and live, work, and play together.

2. Show pictures of different families. Ask students to identify the family members in each. In your discussion reinforce concept of alike/different. Elicit from students ways many families are alike (for example, have children, do things together, parents take care of children) and different (size of family; ages of children—older or younger; living in apartment or house; living in the city or country). Be sensitive to home situations of class members; note that sometimes not all family members live together. Also note that sometimes families change—a baby is born, a grandparent dies, or mother and father don't live in the same house anymore.

3. Ask: "What family did God put you into?" Have each child draw a family picture. Have this caption on the top of each paper for students to trace: "Thank you, God, for my family." You may wish to help students write the names of family members on the picture. Talk about the relationships within the family, such as daughter, sister, grandchild, etc.

4. Display the family pictures and allow opportunity for the children to explain them.

5. **Closure:** "Today we learned about families. We learned that families are part of God's plan and that God gave each of us a special family. How are many families alike? In what ways can families be different?"

• •

Related Activities

1. At a center provide tagboard cutouts of family figures for children to use in "building" different kinds of families and roleplaying family situations.

2. Read a story such as *Some Things Are Different, Some Things Are the Same* by Marya Dantzer-Rosenthal, which compares the homes and families of two friends. Or read books about family relationships. Suggestions: *Mandy's Grandmother* by Liesel Skorpen, *Grandpa* by Barbara Borack, *Sisters* by David McPhail, or two from the Barron's Educational Series by Carme Vendrell and J.M. Parramón, *Family: Parents* and *Family: Grandparents.*

3. At a housekeeping or family living center provide props for acting out various family situations such as making and serving a meal or taking care of children.

4. Tie into math activities by graphing how many people are in the students' families.

LESSON 2: LIKE MOTHER, LIKE DAUGHTER— LIKE FATHER, LIKE SON

Preparation/Materials

- Pictures of families from previous lesson
- Student Activity page
- Optional: Teacher Visual in the back of this book
- Optional: write the poem "Parents Are People" on chart paper and find or sketch pictures to illustrate it.

Objectives

- Students will recognize that a person's gender is part of God's plan.
- Students will understand that girls will have bodies like their mothers and boys like their fathers.
- Students will identify similarities and differences of boys and girls.

Background

In *Horizons Health*, sexuality education is taught at every level within the context of family life. At the kindergarten level, students begin to learn names of sexual organs. They become aware of their own sexual identity and learn to see it as a gift of God.

Although some teachers may prefer to skip over the naming of body parts, teaching correct names for body parts in a matter-of-fact and low-key way is important. It helps teach respect for the body and makes for direct and honest dialogue on health topics. One training program for teachers suggests practicing saying the terms out loud in order to overcome embarrassment.

Be sure to let parents know beforehand what this lesson will cover. Good communication with the home creates trust and allows parents to reinforce what is taught in school.

• •

Lesson

1. **Circle talk.** Refer to the activity page in the Student Workbook showing the pictures of the different families. This time focus on gender differences; lead students to infer that a boy will grow up to have a body like his father and a girl like her mother. Tell students that their gender is part of God's plan for their lives and that being born as boys or girls is a special gift of God.

2. Continue the discussion. Elicit from students physical similarities of boys and girls (for example, both have eyes, ears, hair, etc.). Then talk about physical differences. An optional Teacher Visual naming body parts of boys and girls (breast, navel, penis, vulva, buttocks—not pictured) can be found at the back of this Teacher's Manual. Explain that as girls and boys grow older, some parts of parts of the body change. Boys will start growing beards, and girls will develop breasts. Only girls can be mothers and only boys can be fathers.

3. Use children's literature to further explore the topic of gender and roles, abilities, or interests. Suggested resources: *William's Doll* by Charlotte Zolotow, *Boys & Girls, Girls &*

Boys by Eve Merriam, or *Why Boys and Girls Are Different* by Carol Greene. The following well-known poem on gender and roles, "Parents Are People" by Carol Hall (in *Free to Be . . . You and Me),* reinforces lesson concepts. If you have made a chart of the poem, display it and use as a teaching aid.

Parents Are People
Mommies are people.
People with children.
When mommies were little
They used to be girls,
Like some of you,
But then they grew.

And now mommies are women,
Women with children,
Busy with children
And things that they do.
There are a lot of things
A lot of mommies can do.

Some mommies are ranchers
Or poetry makers
Or doctors or teachers
Or cleaners or bakers.
Some mommies drive taxis
Or sing on TV.
Yes, mommies can be
Almost anything they want to be.

They can't be grandfathers . . .
Or daddies . . .

Daddies are people.
People with children.
When daddies were little
They used to be boys,
Like some of you,
But then they grew.

And now daddies are men,
Men with children,
Busy with children
And things that they do.
There are a lot of things
A lot of daddies can do.

Some daddies are writers
Or grocery sellers
Or painters or welders
Or funny joke tellers.
Some daddies play cello
Or sail on the sea.
Yes, daddies can be
Almost anything they want to be.

They can't be grandmas . . .
Or mommies . . .

Parents are people.
People with children.
When parents were little
They used to be kids,
Like all of you.
But then they grew.

And now parents are grown-ups,
Grown-ups with children
Busy with children
And things that they do.
There are a lot of things
A lot of mommies
And a lot of daddies
And a lot of parents
Can do.

4. **Student Activity**. Refer to the activity page in the Student Workbook. Talk about each picture and ask students to identify the activity or job. Take a poll (another opportunity to integrate with math): Which activities or jobs would students like the best and why? Have students draw a picture on the back of the activity sheet of what they would like to be or do when they grow up.

5. **Closure:** "We learned today that being boys and girls is part of God's plan. Boys will have bodies like their fathers and girls like their mothers. Boys' and girls' bodies are different, but in many other ways boys and girls are the same. In what ways are boys and girls the same?"

• •

Related Activities

- Visit a farm or zoo where baby animals have young. Or better yet hatch eggs or have a litter of animals in the classroom.

LESSON 3: ALL TOGETHER NOW

Preparation/Materials
- Prepare a chart to make with the class. Write the heading "Things Families Do" and paste or draw a few pictures of families (including single parent families) on the top of the chart.
- Optional: clothes and other props for acting out family activities

Objectives
- Students will identify things families commonly do together.
- Students will describe what they can contribute to family life.
- Students will choose to help family members.

Lesson

1. Make an experience chart with the class about things families do together. Show students the prepared chart and briefly discuss the pictures on the chart. Ask class members to name things they do with their families. List their suggestions on the chart; add simple sketches to illustrate. Things to include on the list: eating, shopping, playing, sleeping, traveling, working, praying, reading the Bible, going to church. As you list the last three, talk about why families pray and read the Bible and go to church.

2. Divide class members into "family" groups and have each group act out a family doing something together. If they need ideas, they can look at the sketches on the chart.

3. **Circle talk.** Have the children think about the special roles that people in their own families play. Ask questions like "Who tells funny stories in your family? With whom in your family do you like to play? Who fixes dinner? Who in your family is the tallest/shortest? Who is the silliest/most quiet person in your family? Who sings the loudest?"

   Lead the children to realize that they are important family members. Elicit from class members ways they can or do contribute to family life. Then offer more suggestions. (Include things such as picking up toys, setting the table, emptying wastebaskets, folding laundry, and caring for pets; but also include things such as sharing and showing love.) To make this a lively activity, sing each suggestion to the tune of "Here We Go Round the Mulberry Bush." Add actions to fit the words.

   Example:
   This is the way I fold the clothes (take out the trash, pick up the toys, etc.),
   fold the clothes,
   fold the clothes.
   This is the way I fold the clothes,
   to help my family.

4. **Closure:** "Families need and love each other. Families eat and work and play and pray and go to church together. Children are important family members and can help other family members in many ways."

• •

Related Activities

1. Center idea: have class members make up stories about imaginary families. They can dictate their stories to an adult or into a tape recorder.

2. Plan an open house or special activity (a program, sing-a-long, cook-out, make-a-book day) to which children can bring their families. Involve children in planning, preparation, and making invitations.

3. Invite your own family to visit your class. Children are fascinated with the idea that their teacher has a life and family outside of the classroom.

4. Create a Family Fun Book. (This activity is from *Teaching Young Children Using Themes* [Good Year Books, 1991].)

Help the students define what a joke is and give some examples. Have the children collect jokes from their family members. Some of the favorites can be compiled into a book. Duplicate copies for everyone to take home and share with their families.

LESSON 4: UPS AND DOWNS

Preparation/Materials
- Puppets or other manipulatives
- Plan details of the puppet script.

Objectives
- Students will become aware that healthy family life requires forgiveness and new beginnings.
- Students will predict outcomes of common family situations.
- Students will recognize healthy ways of expressing emotion.

Background
Because of sin, family relationships are marred by quarreling, estrangements, and love-lessness. The previous lesson on family life stressed what families do together and how important it is for family members to pull together. But even young children realize that sometimes family life does not go smoothly, and they need to be reassured that conflicts do not mean that family members don't love each other. Lead students to understand that Christian families can find healing for broken relationships, forgiveness, and the power to make new beginnings. By relying on God's grace and asking for the Spirit's power, families can restore relationships, and family life can be a source of joy.

• •

Lesson

1. Use puppets or or other manipulatives to present a situation in which siblings are quarreling over something.

   Dialogue starter:

   Sal: What did you do that for? I just finished making it! Now it's ruined. Keep your truck out of my way!

   Jamie (unrepentant): I'm a garbage man. I drive a big truck and I have to back up and stop fast and roar around.

   Sal: But you just ruined my city! I just finished building a hospital and a gas station and stores and a fire station.

   Jamie: Well, so what if I knocked a few blocks over? Just fix it.

   Ask the class what each character is feeling and why. Note that living with and loving a family doesn't mean that we don't have problems. Bring in the importance of forgiveness and new beginnings. Stress that God loves us both when we're "nice" and "not-so-nice."

2. Play What If? Give a few common family situations and have students predict outcomes:

   "What if your brother takes most of the car seat and doesn't leave you any room?"

   "What if you're watching TV, and your older brother or sister comes into the room and turns it off?"

"What if you—by mistake—rip the pages of your older brother's or sister's favorite book or magazine?"

"What if you and your younger brother or sister want to play with the same toy?"

Without being moralistic, lead students to become aware of healthy ways to expressing feelings and resolve conflict.

3. Tap the wealth of children's literature on the family, and read and discuss a story about family relationships. A few suggested titles: *A Baby Sister for Frances* by Russell Hoban , *The Berenstain Bears Get in a Fight* by Stan and Jan Berenstain, *It's Not My Fault* by Fritz Brandenberg, *If It Weren't for You* and *Timothy Too* by Charlotte Zolotow, and *Nobody's Perfect, Not Even My Mother* by Norma Simon.

4. **Closure:** "Even though we love the members of our family very much, sometimes they can make us (or we can make them) feel angry or sad. When that happens, what can we do?" (Talk about it, say we're sorry or forgive the other person, and start over.)

● ●

Related Activities

1. Tell a Bible story such as the story of Joseph and his brothers.

2. Center idea: have each student make a My Family booklet. Have students draw pictures of family pets, favorite family foods, and a favorite room at home. Include the pictures of family members made at the beginning of this unit.

3. Extend the lesson to include classroom squabbles. How can conflicts be amicably resolved? Play What If? using classroom situations.

LESSON 5: OUR FAMILIES AND THE FAMILY OF GOD

Preparation/Materials

- Pictures of the family of God (include pictures of people of various races and cultures at prayer, Bible study, or worship)
- For making greeting cards:
  8 1/2" x 11" sheets of construction paper folded in half, one sheet per student
  markers or crayons
  other art materials as desired
- Make a sample greeting card.

Objectives

- Students will recognize that their families are part of the worldwide family of God.
- Students will identify specific activities/beliefs of the family of God.
- Students will choose to show concern for other members of the family of God.

Background

This lesson places the family within the context of the family of God. Christian parents and children are both, by adoption, children of God and part of the worldwide family of God. In this context the family does not exist for its own sake. Rather, as Christians we offer our family life to God and live it in gratitude before God. The family, then, becomes a means of loving and serving God—and others.

• •

Lesson

1. Introduce the concept of the family of God. Show the pictures of the family of God gathered for prayer, Bible study, or worship. Tell students that their families are part of a larger family, the family of God. This family is made up of those—of all ages—who are in Christ, who love and serve God. Stress that this family is worldwide. Have students identify some of the things this family does together (include loving and caring for each other; helping each other; gathering for worship, prayer, and Bible study; and giving so that others can learn about Christ or be clothed, fed, or housed).

   Teach students that this family of God is called the Church. Teach the word as new vocabulary.

2. Sing the song "The Church Is One Big Family." Discuss the meaning of the words. Ask: "How do you know that you belong?" Talk about the meaning of baptism or consecration.

3. **Student activity.** Have students make greeting cards to show caring and concern for other members of the family of God. Show the class a sample card to introduce the activity. Decide what kind of cards to make (birthday, get well, thinking of you) and to whom you will send them. Perhaps brainstorm some simple card messages.

Distribute the folded construction paper. Explain where the children are to draw a picture and where they will put the message. Students can use invented spelling to write the message, or, if you prefer, they can dictate the message to you or a helper.

Be sure to send the cards.

4. **Closure:** "We learned today that our families belong to a bigger family, the family of God. The family of God is made up of people all over the world. What is another name for the family of God? What are some of things the family of God does?"

● ●

Related Activities

- Review the unit by reading the book *Why Boys and Girls Are Different* by Carol Greene. Written from a Christian perspective, it covers much of the unit material—gender and family differences and church family differences.

The Church is One Big Family

Dundee

Margaret C. McNeil

The church is one big fam-i-ly, the church is ev-'ry-
And in this fam-i-ly of love I know that I be-

where. It's peo-ple tall and peo-ple small. The
long. The church is peo-ple lov-ing. I

church is ev-'ry-where.
know that I be-long.

LESSON 6: LIVING WITH DEATH

Preparation/Materials
- Books of choice for Options 2 and 3

Objectives
- Students will recognize that all human beings must die.
- Students will understand that death is the result of sin.
- Students will recognize that in the face of death sadness is a fitting emotion.
- Students will know the comfort of the Christian hope.

Background

The tendency of many North American adults is to try to shield children from the reality of death. They wish to protect children, to keep the children's lives happy and carefree. But death is an inescapable part of life—even for children—in a world marred by sin. Trying to screen out death actually does children a disservice. In fact, with no guidance from parents or teachers, children may struggle with distorted ideas or fears. By guiding their learning about death, adults give children correct information and open the possibility of sharing feelings and fears about death. In the Christian community they can convey the hope of resurrection life in Christ.

Ruth Kopp, in a helpful book entitled *Where Has Grandpa Gone?* helps us understand the concept of death a child has at various age levels. Between the ages of two and six, most children see "everything that moves and has activity as being alive and personal." Since young children also tend to personify abstract ideas, as they become aware of death they think of it as a powerful being that can "come at will and remove people and pets" they love. They develop a variety of ways to fend off the "monster death." Children from about three and four

years old, for example, may hide in the comfort of a security blanket, while from about four to six or seven, they use "fantasy, magic, and wishful thinking" to protect themselves and those they love. But gradually at about six or seven, children acquire what Kopp calls a materialist attitude toward death: they shift their protection against death "from fantasy to the tangible, physical world." In this phase they become aware of their bodies and how they work and find a defense against death in physical fitness—an idea reinforced by North American society. They think that if they are strong and healthy enough, they can prevent illness or injury. During the next phase, from about eight to eleven, children rationally explore their world and the idea of death. They look for reasons and explanations for illnesses, for the most part ignoring the emotions.

So from a young age children are aware of death, and they struggle to deal with it. It isn't possible to shield them from death. However, by sensitively dealing with the subject, we can offer them support and hold out to them the comfort of being a child of God and trusting God to make all things well.

In teaching about death and dying, we should also be aware of the mistaken and unbiblical emphasis in much of the current literature on the topic. Death is usually presented as the natural end of life. We are urged to accept death as natural and, sometimes, even as a beautiful and fitting end to life. It's true, of course, that in the world as we know it—a broken world suffering under the effects of sin—death is a fact and the life cycle ends inevitably in death. But the Bible clearly teaches that death is not a friend but an enemy. Death is the result of human sin. God created us not for death but for life. Christians believe Christ has removed the sting of death and in him we already have new life that never ends. Christ's resurrection body is the guarantee of the resurrection of our bodies.

This lesson has been developed for grades K-2. It provides several options and lists of resources from which to choose. Your choices will depend on the grade level, on what approach you are comfortable with, and on your classroom situation. At the kindergarten level we suggest you plan a session on the subject of death at the close of this unit on the family,

using the resources of Option 2 or 3. You may wish to use other resources when the subject of death comes up naturally in the classroom or fits in with Bible studies (for example, with a lesson on the death of Elijah or with your celebration of Easter). Since there is not much literature on death written from a Christian perspective, bear in mind that it is crucial to critically read the books listed below and to provide Christian perspective through comments and discussion.

● ●

Lesson

Option 1. Tell about the loss of someone you know, how sad you felt and how you missed the person. Talk about the source of your comfort and how that helped you.

Option 2. Use the subject of the death of pets to lead into a general discussion of death. Tell students about a pet you or one of your family members had that died, and read one of the many excellent books available on the death of a pet. Although these books focus on the death of pets, many of them obliquely refer to death of people.

Father's Laika by Mats Wahl
Jim's Dog Muffins by Miriam Cohen
Goodbye, Max by Holly Keller
The Dead Bird by Margaret Wise Brown
Better With Two by Catherine Stock
It Must Hurt a Lot: A Child's Book About Death by Doris Sanford

After reading the story, have students identify some of the feelings that the main character or characters had. Allow time for students to ask questions or to talk about family pets that have died. Stress that sadness is an appropriate feeling when a loved pet dies.

Option 3. Introduce the idea of change or loss by reading a book about moving and loss entailed by the ones who are moving or staying. Use this as a starting point for discussing loss through death.

We Are Best Friends by Aliki
Pip Moves Away by Myra Berry Brown
My Friend William Moved Away by Martha Hickman
Ira Says Goodbye by Bernard Waber
Janey by Charlotte Zolotow
Mitchell Is Moving by Marjorie Sharmat
Moving Molly by Shirley Hughes
Nana Upstairs, Nana Downstairs by Tomie dePaola

Option 4. Read a book dealing with human death. Although these books deal with death in a sensitive way, none of them is written from a Christian perspective. Thus it is important to read the books critically and spend time discussing the Christian hope in the face of death.

Goodbye Rune by Marit Kaldhol and Wenche Oyen

My Grandma Leonie by Bijou LeTord

Grandpa's Slide Show by Deborah Gould

Marianne's Grandmother by Bettina Egger

I Had a Friend Named Peter: Talking to Children About Death by Janice Cohn

Everett Anderson's Goodbye by Lucille Clifton

Option 5. Use an occasion that naturally arises in the classroom, the death of a relative or friend of a class member, to talk about the subject of death. Be sure to stress the Christian hope, but also talk about feelings connected with death. Although Christians believe in new and eternal life in Christ, grief is nonetheless a fitting response to the loss of a loved one. Identify concrete ways to help the one who is grieving.

Use appropriate Scripture passages such as Psalm 23 or the story of Jesus' resurrection as a basis for continued discussion. And sing appropriate songs about Christ's resurrection or about the comfort of the Christian hope. A few suggested titles:

"Children of the Heavenly Father" (*Psalter Hymnal*, 440; *Songs of God's Love*, 62)

"He's Got the Whole World in His Hands" (*Songs of God's Love*, 56)

"The Lord's My Shepherd" (*Proclaim 2*, 16; *Psalter Hymnal*, 161; alternate tune, *Children's Hymnbook*, 19)

"Christ the Lord Is Risen Today" (*Proclaim 2*, 25)

Unit 3

Getting Along With Others

Lesson 1:   Mind Your Manners

Lesson 2:   Listening

Lesson 3:   Sharing

Lesson 4:   Cooperating

Goals

- Students will develop skills for getting along with others.
- Students will develop Christian attitudes toward others.
- Students will choose to treat others in a caring, courteous way.

Background

Christians recognize the power of sin to break down communication, mar relationships, and disrupt community. But Christians believe that the risen Christ has power to transform and renew us and our relationship to God and to others. In this context "getting along with others" means much more than learning a set of skills (although interpersonal skills are important) or following a set of specific behavior patterns.

The apostle Paul addresses the problem of interpersonal relationships in these words: "But the fruit of the Spirit is love, joy, peace, patience, kindness, goodness, faithfulness, gentleness and self-control. . . . Since we live by the Spirit, let us keep in step with the Spirit. Let us not become conceited, provoking and envying each other" (Galatians 5: 22, 25, 26). Keeping in step with the Spirit will lead us away from self-centeredness—and toward the self-control and concern for others necessary for living in community.

This unit, then, is not a Dale Carnegie mini-course. The lessons are not meant to promote a self-serving "you scratch my back and I'll scratch yours" outlook. Rather, by giving students the opportunity to show courtesy, kindness, and love to others and to learn about getting along with others, we are nurturing them in the life of the Spirit.

Vocabulary

Integrate the following suggested vocabulary:

manners	please	cooperate	share/sharing
good	listen	bad	

Unit Resources

Gibbs, Jeanne. *Tribes: A Process for Social Development and Cooperative Learning.* Santa Rosa, Calif.: Center Source Publications, 1987.

Although the scope of this book is much broader than the content of this unit, its suggestions for cooperative activities make it a helpful teacher resource. Order from the publisher: 305 Tesconi Circle, Santa Rosa, California 95401.

Hill, Susan and Tim. *The Collaborative Classroom: A Guide to Co-operative Learning.* Portsmouth, N.H.: Heinemann, 1990.

This book is "about people learning and working together, rather than alone." A valuable resource, not only for unit activities but also for establishing a truly cooperative classroom.

Hiller, Ron. *Ronno's "Getting Along" Theme Pack.* Kitchener, Ont.: Song Support, 1991.

Includes "Let's Co-operate" and "The Good Manners Song," two original songs tying in with the unit theme. In the pack are a 38-page booklet with the piano/vocal score and an audiocassette. Order from the publisher: Station C, Box 722, Kitchener, Ontario, Canada N2G 4B6 or Suite 162, 255 Great Arrow Ave., Buffalo, New York 14207-3081.

Prutzman, Priscilla, and others. *Friendly Classroom for a Small Planet: A Handbook on Creative Approaches to Living and Problem Solving for Children.* Philadelphia: New Society Publishers, 1988.

> Children's Creative Response to Conflict, an organization with Quaker roots, developed this resource. It contains suggestions and activities for building community, learning to communicate, and promoting self-awareness and empathy. Available from the publisher: P.O. Box 582, Santa Cruz, California 95061.

Lesson Resources

Lesson 1

Aliki. *Manners.* New York: Greenwillow, 1990.

> Amusing illustrations and a handwritten text combine for a delightful look at manners.

Baker, Eugene. *Your Manners Are Showing.* Cincinnati: Standard, 1980.

Berenstain, Stan and Jan. *The Berenstain Bears Forget Their Manners.* New York: Random, 1986.

Brown, Marc, and Stephen Krensky. *Perfect Pigs: An Introduction to Manners.* New York: Atlantic Monthly Press, 1983.

Dellinger, Annetta E. *Good Manners for God's Children.* St. Louis: Concordia, 1984.

Hoban, Russell. *Dinner at Alberta's.* New York: Harper/Collins, 1977.

> Because Arthur the crocodile eats like a beast, his family is trying to shape up his table manners for dinner at Alberta's.

Leaf, Munro. *Manners Can Be Fun.* 3rd ed. New York: Harper Junior Books, 1985.

Odor, Ruth S. *A Child's Books of Manners.* A Happy Day book. Cincinnati: Standard, 1990.

Simon, Norma. *What Do I Say?* Niles, Ill.: Whitman, 1983.

Lesson 3

Raffi. *Singable Songbook.* New York: Crown, 1988.

> Students will enjoy the "Sharing Song" from this collection.

Lesson 4

Reihecky, Janet. *Cooperation: Values to Live by.* Chicago: Childrens Press, 1990.

> Pictures situations in which cooperation is necessary; a good discussion starter.

LESSON 1: MIND YOUR MANNERS

Preparation/Materials

- Puppets or other manipulatives
- For a bulletin board about good manners: a background and title, as desired, birds, flowers, and butterflies made of construction paper, at least one example of each
- Optional: Book about manners to read aloud

Objectives

- Students will identify good manners and bad manners in specific situations.
- Students will become aware of the effect of good/bad manners on feelings.
- Students will choose to use good manners.

Background

Showing courtesy is one way of loving our neighbors. Waiting our turn in line, thanking someone for help, excusing ourselves when we reach or step in front of someone are all ways of demonstrating our concern for others. Courtesy takes the other person's feelings and needs into account, recognizes the contribution or help of others, and often puts others first. As you teach this lesson, stress that basic courtesy is treating others the same way you would like to be treated.

But there is another aspect of courtesy: every society has a set of rules that govern a variety of social situations. Knowing these rules and feeling comfortable with them will help children feel more at ease socially. Give students opportunity, especially during this unit, to practice social skills and develop self-confidence.

• •

Lesson

1. Use puppets or other manipulatives to act out a series of situations in which the characters show bad manners.

   Suggested situations:
   The two characters meet. One says, "Hi (name)," but the other mumbles something and walks on.
   One character gives an object (toy, color crayons, cookie) to the other. The other person doesn't say thank you or show any appreciation.
   One character demands ("I want" or "Gimme") the use of some commonly shared classroom material such as crayons or scissors.
   One bumps into the other but doesn't apologize or stop to help.

   Stop after each situation and ask for a better way for the character to speak or respond. Make the connection between manners and feelings. Then redo the scene with characters using good manners. In the first suggested situation, for example, teach students to look at the greeter and respond using the person's name—if they know it. If the greeter is an adult with whom they are not on a first-name basis, they should use Mr., Ms., or Mrs. Perhaps have students practice saying some names of school staff together. Knowing how to respond helps to develop social self-confidence.

2. Optional: Reinforce the good manners discussed in step 1 by reading a book about manners. Suggested titles: *Manners* by Aliki, *Perfect Pigs: An Introduction to Manners* by Marc Brown and Stephen Krensky, *The Berenstain Bears Forget Their Manners* by Stan and Jan Berenstain, *What Do I Say?* by Norma Simon, *Manners Can Be Fun* by Munro Leaf, *Good Manners for God's Children* by Annetta E. Dellinger, or *Your Manners Are Showing* by Eugene Baker.

3. To encourage students to follow up on the lesson, tell them that you're going to try to "catch" them using good manners (as the unit progresses add other positive behaviors). Make a bulletin board on which you will post names of those you catch. Write the names on construction paper flowers, butterflies, birds, or trees to gradually create a garden. Identify the behavior with a short sentence (for example, "Sandy thanked Mary for the crayon") or a simple picture. Show students samples of the construction paper figures to create interest in the project.

4. **Closure:** "Today we talked about manners—good manners and bad manners. What is one way to show good manners? (Call on several volunteers to each name one way.) How does it make you feel when people use bad manners? What about good manners?"

● ●

Related Activities

1. Invite a school staff member or parent to the classroom and have several student volunteers practice using good manners to greet him or her.

2. Center idea: encourage students at the play or drama/dress-up center to practice good manners by acting out the situations covered in the puppet scenes. Or make the puppets available for students to use in reenacting the scenes.

LESSON 2: LISTENING

Preparation/Materials
- Toy telephones, one for each pair of students
- Optional: paper shapes, blocks, or other objects in various colors, the same number and color for each student

Objectives
- Students will learn steps to careful listening.
- Students will practice listening to each other.

Background

"Listening is a skill that can be learned and an art that can be mastered…. We owe it to ourselves to make it our best language art!" This quotation from a popular book on teaching listening to children turns the purpose of listening on its head. Listening is not something we owe to ourselves. Listening to others is one way of loving them. Active listening means that we are receptive to others, that we value them and their ideas. This lesson makes students aware of what's involved in listening and why listening is important. It helps them practice and improve their listening skills. But keep the emphasis of the lesson straight, for although learning listening skills can make us more conscious of what's going on in the communication process, skills are no substitute for sincere interest and concern.

• •

Lesson

1. Begin by playing a listening game. Suggestions:

   - Call on individual students to repeat a list of two or three items you name in a sentence. For example:

     "I'm going to the store. I'm going to buy bread, apples, and milk. What am I going to buy at the store?"

     "I'm going to the park. I'm going to play on the seesaw, the slide, and the merry-go-round. What am I going to play on?"

     "I'm going to play in the snow. I need my hat, jacket, and boots. What do I need?"

     "I'm going to visit my grandmother. I'm going to take my blanket, pillow, and pajamas. What am I going to take?"

   - Follow up on the first exercise by playing the game I'm Going on a Trip. The first person says, "I'm going on a trip and I'm taking my teddy bear along." The second person repeats what the first person said and then adds a new item to the list (I'm going on a trip and I'm taking my teddy bear and toothbrush along). Continue around the circle in this way with each person adding a new item. This game highlights the importance of looking at each speaker as the list of items gets longer. Looking at the speaker is a memory help.

   - Give students a set of shapes or objects similar in color (for example, each child should have two yellow, blue, and red squares). Name colors and have students arrange (specify left to right) the shapes or objects in that order. For example, if you say,"Red, yellow, blue, red," students should arrange shapes in that order. To make the game more complex, include different shapes (red square, blue circle, yellow circle).

2. **Circle time.** Form a listening circle. Tell the children that this is a listening circle. Ask them what we do when we listen. Stress that we look (point to eyes) at the speaker and pay attention (point to ears) to what he or she is saying.

   Have students practice listening to each other. Go around the circle asking students questions about their preferences (ask questions that can be answered in a few words). Ask for example: "What's your favorite game (color, food, toy)?" When necessary, point to eyes and ears as a reminder to listen with full attention. Make a brief comment or nod after each speaker is finished.

   At the end of the activity, ask volunteers to say what new thing(s) they learned about other class members. Talk about how people feel when others take the time to listen to them.

3. Provide toy telephones and have students carry on conversations with each other. Encourage talking by turns and listening to each other. (This could be a center activity.)

4. **Closure:** "When we listen to people, we stop what we're doing, look at them, and pay attention to what they're saying. When we listen to others, they know that we care about them."

● ●

Related Activities

1. Have pairs of students play a listening game in which one gives directions and the other listens and follows the directions. For example, ask each pair to sit back to back. Each of the pair makes a necklace; with a shoelace and large wooden beads. One of the students tells the other what color bead to use. The finished necklaces should be exactly the same. If time permits, students can switch roles and make another necklace. (Adapted from *The New Kindergarten* by Jean Marzollo [Harper, 1987].)

2. Take pictures (or have a parent or teacher aide do this) of students listening, sharing (Lesson 3), and cooperating (Lesson 4). Make a class book so that students can see themselves doing these activities.

LESSON 3: SHARING

Preparation/Materials

- Student Activity page
- Chart paper
- Write a letter asking parents to send 1 cup of a snack such as raisins, pretzels, or peanuts for sharing feast.
- One large bowl
- Small plates or cups, one for each student
- Plan and collect materials for simple sharing activity.
- Optional: bring something of your own to share with the class.

Objectives

- Students will develop increased understanding of what it means to share.
- Students will identify ways to share in the classroom.
- Students will practice sharing.

Background

Because egocentrism is a normal characteristic of early childhood, sharing is a very difficult concept for young children to grasp. Some think sharing means that others should give them what they want; some only see that they must give up something. Children begin to understand sharing by learning to take turns and to see how other children enjoy their turns. Gradually they come to understand the position and viewpoint of another person. Children around the age of five become less possessive about objects but more possessive about people. Sharing friends may be very difficult for some kindergartners. Use this lesson to encourage them in the direction of sharing, of loving their neighbors.

• •

Lesson

1. **Student activity.** Refer to the activity page in the Student Workbook showing the picture of children sharing. Ask class members to describe the picture and elicit the response that the children in the picture are sharing. Teach the word share. Have the students color the activity sheet.

2. Make an experience chart, brainstorming things the class members already share (even though usually students may be taking turns with the materials). Draw simple pictures of the items (center materials, books, and so on) on the chart. As you work on the chart together, identify ways to improve classroom sharing.

3. If you have brought something to share with the class, show it to the class and then place it on a table or in a center for the children to play with later.

4. Prepare the sharing feast. Have each child pour snack ingredients into a large bowl. If one child has forgotten to bring something, reassure him or her that there will be enough to share. Perhaps assign this child the task of stirring the mix together. Let the children take turns coming up and helping themselves to a portion of the mix. (If you have lots of leftovers, you may consider sharing with another classroom.

5. **Closure:** "Today we talked about ways we can share in the classroom. When we take turns, we all can use something (give a classroom example). How did we share in class today?"

● ●

Related Activities

1. Sing songs about sharing. Try the following piggyback song. Use the tune to "Did You Ever See a Lassie?" and the following words:

   "Did you ever share a toy, a toy, a toy?"
   (repeat three times)
   "Now you tell me when."

   Have a volunteer tell about a time he or she shared. Then repeat the song naming what was shared (game, book, picture, snack).

   Or sing "The Sharing Song" by Raffi or obtain the audiocassette and listen and sing along.

2. Encourage children to bring books from home that they would be willing to share with other class members for a few days or a week. Send a letter home to parents with suggested topics that relate to classroom studies. As each child brings in books, have him or her show it to the class and tell what it is about. Ask the child to find a place for it in the book nook.

LESSON 4: COOPERATING

Preparation/Materials
- Rhythm instruments (striking variety), one for each pair of students

Objectives
- Students will understand what it means to cooperate.
- Students will make cooperative music.

Lesson

1. Write the word *cooperate* on the board. Ask: "Do you know what it means to cooperate?" Give students the opportunity to respond. Explain that to cooperate means to work together. Give an example of a typical class situation in which class members cooperate (straightening class equipment or working together to complete class projects). Tell the students that today they will cooperate to make beautiful music.

2. Pass out the rhythm instruments, giving one instrument to each pair of children. Encourage them to experiment with making music by sharing and cooperating. Suggest that they find a way that they can both play the instrument at the same time, either by taking turns being the holder and the striker or by having one student tap the instrument against the other's hand. Praise their success and point out the different ways they found to cooperate.

3. Conclude by having the children cooperate with their instrument to keep the beat while chanting, "It's great! It's great! We can all cooperate!"

4. **Closure:** "When we cooperate, we work together to do something. How did the whole class cooperate today?"

Related Activities

1. Have each class member draw a picture of himself or herself cooperating with a partner to make beautiful music. Or have the partners work together on one drawing to show how they cooperated.

2. Make submarine sandwiches as a cooperative venture.

Collect these ingredients (contact parents)
    submarine rolls, one for every four students
    cheese slices, 2-3 per roll
    luncheon meat, 2-3 per roll
    sliced tomatoes, optional
    lettuce, 2 pieces per roll
    serving plates or napkins
    plastic knives
    one cutting knife

Divide ingredients (for example, cheese for each group) and place them in small plastic bags.

Divide the class into small groups and have each group make a submarine sandwich to share. Set out the ingredients in a central place. Call on a child from each group to get an ingredient and put it on the group's roll.

Cut up the sandwiches and enjoy the snack.

Unit 4

Knowing My Body

Goals

- Students will become aware of their five senses as the way they communicate with the world around them.
- Students will respond with awe and praise to God their Creator.

Background

In *Beyond Doubt* (Christian Reformed Board of Publications, 1980) Cornelius Plantinga tells an anecdote about Whittaker Chambers, a dedicated atheist. One day when Chambers was watching his child as she sat in her high chair, "he found himself staring with fascination at his daughter's tiny, intricate ear. It seemed to him a marvel. Only a *planner* could have planned that ear." This experience "set Chambers on the road to belief."

The human body is truly amazing. And it's very smart. In fact, it's brilliant. It performs to a large extent "on its own." The heart beats, lungs breathe, stomach digests, kidneys purify—all without our even thinking about it. When we study the human body—its parts, processes, growth, and development, we cannot help but wonder at the complexity of its design. But like Chambers, our study should lead us to marvel not only at the body, but at the God who created it.

God has given us life, and that life is mysteriously and inextricably linked to a body so complex that we will never completely understand it. Our fitting response is awe and wonder and praise to God, the Creator. "I will praise you," said the Psalmist, "because I am fearfully and wonderfully made; your works are wonderful, I know that full well" (Psalm 139:14).

Vocabulary

Integrate the following suggested vocabulary:

sense(s)	eyes	ears	nose
see	tongue	mouth	hand
hear	skin	salty	body
touch	sweet	sour	bitter
smell	taste		

Unit Resources

You and Your Five Senses. Filmstrip/audiocassette. Disney Educational Products.
   An overview of the senses, which compares human senses to that of animals. A seven-minute filmstrip.

Five Senses Pictures.
   This bulletin board set with resource guide has suggestions for over 30 student activities.

Lesson Resources

Lesson 1

Kellogg, Steven. *Much Bigger Than Martin.* New York: Dial, 1976.
A boy gets satisfaction from imagining being bigger than his brother.

Kraus, Ruth. *The Growing Story.* New York: Harper, 1947.
A farm boy's clothes no longer fit.

Martin, Bill, Jr., and John Archambault. *Here Are My Hands.* New York: Holt, 1987.
Describes feelings of children about the different parts of their bodies.

Prelutsky, Jack, compiler. *Read-Aloud Rhymes for the Very Young.* New York: Knopf, 1986.
Poems about growing include "Something About Me," "The Wish," "Big," and "My Sister Laura."

Lesson 2

Aliki. *My Five Senses.* New York: Crowell, 1962.
Explores the enjoyment of different sounds, tastes, sights, smells, and touches.

Brenner, Barbara. *Faces.* New York: Dutton, 1970.
Explains what the eyes, ears, nose, and mouth are used for.

Tudor, Tasha. *First Delights—A Book About the Five Senses.* New York: Putnam, 1988.

Lesson 3

Hoban, Tana. *Is It Red? Is It Yellow? Is It Blue?* New York: Greenwillow, 1978.

Martin, Bill, Jr. *Brown Bear, Brown Bear, What Do You See?* New York: Holt, 1983.

Moncure, Jane. *The Look Book.* Chicago: Childrens Press, 1982.

Rius, Maria, J.J. Puig, and J.M. Parramón. *The Five Senses: Sight.* Toronto/New York: Barron's, 1985.

Thigpen, Thomas. *Colors of Creation.* Weston, Ont./Elgin, Ill.: Cook, 1990.

Ziefert, Harriet. *Sarah's Questions.* New York: Lothrop, 1986.
A mother and daughter play I Spy as they go for a walk.

Lesson 4

Moncure, Jane. *What Your Nose Knows!* Chicago: Childrens Press, 1982.

Perkins, Al. *The Nose Book.* New York: Random, 1970.

Petty, Kate, and Lisa Kopper. *What's That Smell?* New York: Watts, 1987.

Pluckrose, Henry. *Think About Smelling.* New York: Watts, 1983.

Rius, Maria, J.J. Puig, and J.M. Parramón. *The Five Senses: Smell.* Toronto/New York: Barron's, 1985.

What Do I Smell and Taste? Filmstrip/audiocassette. Encyclopedia Britannica.
Explains how our senses help us identify foods and other objects.

Lesson 5

Brown, Margaret Wise. *The Noisy Book.* New York: Harper, 1939.

Carle, Eric. The *Very Quiet Cricket: A Multi-Sensory Book.* New York: Philomel, 1990.
A young cricket rubs his wings together but can't make a sound until he meets another very quiet cricket. Teachers could use the form of this story for writing a class story.

Hearn, Emily. *Whoosh! I Hear a Sound.* Toronto: Annick Press, 1983.

McMillan, Bruce. *One Sun: A Book of Terse Verse.* New York: Scholastic/Holiday House, 1991.
Wonderful photos illustrate two-word rhymes.

Martin, Bill, Jr. and John Archambault. *Listen to the Rain.* New York: Holt, 1989.

Martin, Bill, Jr. *Polar Bear, Polar Bear, What Do You Hear?* New York: Holt, 1991.
Illustrated by Eric Carle, this book helps preschoolers put animals together with the noises they make. For ages 2-5.

Perkins, Al. *The Ear Book.* New York: Random, 1968.

Rius, Maria, J.J. Puig, and J.M. Parramón. *The Five Senses: Hearing.* Toronto/New York: Barron's, 1985.

Rylant, Cynthia. *Night in the Country.* New York: Bradbury, 1986.

Lesson 6

Moncure, Jane. *A Tasting Party.* Chicago: Childrens Press, 1982.

Pluckrose, Henry. *Think About Tasting.* New York: Watts, 1986.
A book of photographs about tasting.

Rius, Maria, J.J. Puig, and J.M. Parramón. *The Five Senses: Taste.* Toronto/New York: Barron's, 1985.

Ziefert, Harriet. *What Do I Taste: The Five Senses.* New York: Bantam, 1988.

Lesson 7

Aliki. *My Hands.* Rev. ed. New York: Harper, 1990.

Brown, Marcia. *Touch Will Tell.* New York: Watts, 1979.

Hoban, Tana. *Is It Rough? Is It Smooth? Is It Shiny?* New York: Greenwillow, 1984.

Moncure, Jane. *The Touch Book.* Chicago: Childrens Press, 1982.

Rius, Maria, J.J. Puig, and J.M. Parramón. *The Five Senses: Touch.* Toronto/New York: Barron's, 1985.

Showers, Paul. *Find Out by Touching.* Let's Read and Find Out Science Series. New York: Harper Junior, 1961.

You and Your Sense of Touch. Filmstrip/audiocassette. Disney Educational Products.
Describes how warmth, cold, pressure, and pain keep us healthy and safe. Running time of about seven minutes.

LESSON 1: DEVELOPING BODY AWARENESS

Preparation/Materials
- Paper strips for making chains to measure height of each student
- Baby clothes
- Optional: music to accompany body movements

Objectives
- Students will become aware of how their bodies move.
- Students will recognize that God has designed bodies to grow.
- Students will conclude that they are growing.

Lesson

1. Begin this unit on growth and development with movement activities to develop body awareness. Have students shake their arms, wiggle their fingers and toes, stick out their tongues, blink their eyes, clap their hands, or make other movements. You may wish to play music to accompany the movements. During the activity make class members aware of the various parts of their bodies.

2. **Circle talk.** Focus on how amazing our bodies are, how by God's design all the different parts work together so that we can do many different things. Note that another amazing thing about us is the way we grow. Show students the baby clothes and ask: "Did you ever wear clothes that small? Can you still wear clothes that small?" Contrast the way we outgrow clothes to the wonderful way our skin keeps growing. (Recall the "Just Me" poem in Unit 1.) Tell students that our bones and other parts keep growing also. Note that although we're alike in that we all grow, we're different because we don't grow exactly the same amount.

3. Teach the following verse. Make up motions to fit the words:

   > Growing, growing,
   > Growing taller,
   > Growing everyday.
   > Reaching, reaching,
   > Reaching higher,
   > Reaching all the way.
   > If I grow up to the ceiling
   > What will my (mother, father, teacher) say?

   Ask students: "What can you do now that you couldn't do when you were smaller? What things do you want to learn to do?"

4. Have students "measure" their own height. Provide paper strips and have each student make a paper chain that corresponds to his or her height. Staple each finished chain to a small piece of construction paper with the student's name. Then display the chains on the classroom wall with the chains touching the floor.

5. **Closure:** "God made our bodies in an amazing way. All the different parts work together and can grow. How do we know we've grown? We don't all grow the same amount at the same time. That's why the people in our class are all different sizes."

• •

Related Activities

1. Ask students to bring baby pictures to class. Have the class try to match baby pictures and class members.

2. Center idea: provide pictures showing development for students to place in sequence. Cut out magazine pictures of individuals at different stages of growth and development, scramble the pictures, and have students arrange the pictures sequentially.

3. Bring in pictures of yourself from baby to child to adolescent to adult. Show the photos to the class and tell the children about something you learned to do at each stage of development. Scramble the pictures and have the children place them back in sequence.

4. Read books and poems about growing: *Here Are My Hands* by Bill Martin, Jr. and John Archambault; *The Growing Story* by Ruth Krauss; and *Much Bigger Than Martin* by Steven Kellogg; "Something About Me," "The Wish," "Big," and "My Sister Laura" in *Read-Aloud Rhymes for the Very Young*.

LESSON 2: THE FIVE SENSES – INTRODUCTION

Preparation/Materials
- Story about the five senses
- Magazine pictures depicting each of the five senses
- Optional: make a poster illustrating the song "God Gave Me Eyes" for a unit teaching aid.

Objectives
- Students will become aware of their senses.
- Students will identify each of the five senses and the body part associated with each.
- Students will react with thankfulness to God for their senses.

Lesson

1. Introduce the five senses by reading to the class one of the many excellent books available on the topic. Suggestions: *My Five Senses* by Aliki, *Tasha Tudor's First Delights—A Book about the Five Senses*, or *Faces* by Barbara Brenner.

2. **Circle talk.** Use visuals to introduce each sense and relate it to the corresponding sense organ. Show the pictures one at a time and ask students to identify each sense. Teach the word *sense*. Display the visuals in a prominent place in the classroom while teaching this unit.

3. Teach Margaret Crain's song about the five senses. As you sing, have students touch the body part associated with each sense. Students will have opportunity to sing the song frequently during the unit.

4. **Closure:** "We learned today that we have five senses. We see with our eyes, hear with our ears, taste with our mouths, smell with our noses, and touch with our hands or skin. We're going to learn more about each of the senses later."

Related Activities

- Show students magazine pictures related to one of the senses (flower, food, pet, fire, beverage, sand, smoke) and have students decide which sense is involved. (In many cases, more than one sense can be named.) Explain that the senses work together. Consider having students place each of the pictures around or under the lesson visual depicting the corresponding sense.

God Gave Me Eyes

M.L.C.

Magaret L. Crain

Blue, blue sky, Oh, I can see the sky.
Red, red rose, Oh, I can smell a rose.
Ding, dong, bell, Oh, I can hear a bell.
Yum, Yum, Yum, Oh, I can taste ice cream.
Mew, mew, mew, My kit-ty's fur is soft.

God gave me eyes So I can see the sky.
God gave a nose So I can smell a rose.
God gave me ears So I can hear a bell.
God gave a tongue So I can taste ice cream.
God gave me hands So I can feel how soft.

LESSON 3: SENSE OF SIGHT

Preparation/Materials

- Music to accompany the game "I See"
- Chart paper
- Student Activities 1 & 2

Objectives

- Students will associate the sense of sight with the eyes.
- Students will identify ways to protect eyes from injury.

• •

Lesson

1. Begin with a lively game of "I See." Have the class move to music. Occasionally stop the music. When the music stops, students should freeze, staring straight ahead. Ask one student, "What do you see?" The child answers by describing one thing in his or her line of frozen vision (or if you prefer one color he or she sees). The rest of the students have three tries to guess what the object is. Then continue playing the game.

2. **Circle time.** Ask: "Why do you think God gave us eyes?" Give students time to respond. Then talk about what we do with our eyes: see the amazing world that God created. Ask students to name some specific things that they like to see or look at.

    Compare our eyes to windows and explain that our eyes are our windows on God's world. Identify some things our eyes help us do. Include ways our eyes help to keep us safe (for example, see oncoming traffic, obstacles, traffic lights). Teach the words *see* and *eyes*.

3. Work with the class to make a chart of ways to protect our eyes from injury. Note that God created our eyes in such a way that they would protect themselves with eyelids and eyelashes. Draw simple pictures on the chart to illustrate the safety rules.

    Rules to include:
    Carry sharp objects such as scissors and pencils point down.
    Don't point sharp things at others.
    Don't run with sharp things.
    If you get something in your eye, get help. Don't rub your eye.
    Sometimes our eyes need eyeglasses to help them do their work. Be careful around glasses—don't knock others' eyeglasses.

4. **Student activity.** Refer to Student Activities 1 and 2 in the Student Workbook, which will be the first two pages of a student booklet about the five senses. Explain that the words printed on Student Activity 1 are a verse about the sense of sight from the song

"God Gave Me Eyes." Sing the verse together. Have students trace the words *I can see.* Then ask students to color Student Activity 2. Keep the completed papers in student folders.

5. **Closure:** "Today we talked about seeing. What do we see with? Our eyes. Our eyes are our windows on God's creation, aren't they? Our eyes help to keep us safe. What are some ways to take care of our eyes?"

• •

Related Activities

1. Enjoy books about the sense of sight. Some suggested book titles: *Brown Bear, Brown Bear, What Do You See?* by Bill Martin, Jr., *Sarah's Questions* by Harriet Ziefert, *Is It Red? Is It Yellow? Is It Blue?* by Tana Hoban, *The Look Book* by Jane Moncure, and *Colors of Creation* by Thomas Thigpen.

2. Center idea: provide about five or six magnifying glasses and a number of small items for students to closely examine.

3. Show the class large pictures with plenty of detail. Ask students what they see in each picture. Have them look closely and describe specifics. Direct them to begin their description by saying, "I see (name of object)." Elicit details by asking leading questions ("Is is big or small? What color is it?").

LESSON 4: SENSE OF SMELL

Preparation/Materials
- A glass of water and a glass of white vinegar
- Student Activities 1 & 2

Objectives
- Students will identify the nose as the body part associated with the sense of smell.
- Students will discriminate between different smells.
- Students will recognize the role of the sense of smell in keeping us safe.

● ●

Lesson

1. Show students a glass of water and a glass of white vinegar. Then ask them what they think the two glasses contain (they will probably say the glasses contain water). Let them take turns smelling the contents of the two glasses. Elicit from students how they know that one liquid is not water. Can they identify both liquids by their sense of smell?

2. Take students on an imaginary walk and identify the smells on the way. Get them involved by chanting together: "We're going for a walk. Where are we going? We're going to a bakery. What do we smell? We smell bread." Suggest (or let students suggest) other bakery smells to continue the chant. Move on from the bakery to another location such as a garage (gasoline), park (flowers, skunk, grass), or kitchen (onions, fish or chicken frying).

3. Talk about ways our sense of smell can keep us safe (smelling smoke or something burning).

4. **Student activity.** Refer to Activities 1 and 2 in the Student Workbook. Have students make the next pages of the senses booklet. Read and sing the second verse of the five senses song. Students can trace the words *I can smell* in Student Activity 1 and color Student Activity 2.

5. **Closure:** "One of our five senses is the sense of smell. There are many wonderful smells. (Student can name some favorite smells.) One reason God gives us a sense of smell is to help keep us safe."

• •

Related Activities

1. Center idea: have a set of mystery bottles for students to smell. Suggested contents: lemon, peppermint, pickle, cinnamon, vinegar, perfume. Consider color coding the bottles and providing students with an activity sheet showing the colors in corresponding order so that students can either draw pictures of what they think they are smelling or simply draw a happy or unhappy face to record their reaction to the smell. Integrate with math by graphing reactions.

2. Read books about the sense of smell. Some suggested titles are: *What Your Nose Knows!* by Jane Moncure, *Think About Smelling* (photos) by Henry Pluckrose, *The Nose Book* by Al Perkins, and *What's That Smell?* by Kate Petty and Lisa Kopper, and *The Five Senses: Smell* by Rius, Puig, and Parramón.

3. Make sachets for students to give as gifts or to put in their dresser drawers.

LESSON 5: SENSE OF HEARING

Preparation/Materials

- Make an audio recording of a variety of sounds: water running, door closing, engine running, pencil tapping, bell or telephone ringing, and keys jangling.
- Tape recorder
- Student Activities 1 & 2

Objectives

- Students will identify ears as the body part associated with sense of hearing.
- Students will discriminate different sounds with their sense of hearing.
- Students will recognize that our hearing helps to protect us.

• •

Lesson

1. Play the audio recording of various sounds. After playing each sound, stop the tape and let class members guess what the sound is.

2. **Circle time.** Recall the body part that we hear with. Then ask students to tell some of their favorite sounds and offer examples of some of your own favorite sounds. Tell students that we know some things God likes to hear—people praising and thanking him.

3. Explain how our hearing can help to protect us by warning us. Work with the class to develop a list of some common warning sounds: someone calling for help or shouting an alarm, fire alarm, police or ambulance siren, car horn, train whistle and railroad crossing bell, car horn, growling of a dog, or hissing of a cat.

   Note that we take care of our sense of hearing by not putting things in our ears and by washing them with a washcloth wrapped around a finger—and nothing smaller.

4. Sing "The Noise Song" with the class. Students will find this song great fun.

5. **Student activity.** Refer to Activities 1 and 2 in the Student Workbook. Have students complete the next pages of the five senses booklet. Read or sing the verse about hearing, and have class members trace the words *I can hear* in Student Activity 1. Talk about the wide variety of bells—bicycle and tricycle bells, church bells, Christmas bells, bells on horses, cow bells. Have the students color Student Activity 2. Keep the completed papers in the students' folders.

6. **Closure:** "We hear with our ears. What are some sounds we like to hear? What are some sounds that help keep us safe?"

● ●

Related Activities

1. Play a listening game called Cat and Mouse. Have the class sit in a circle. One person, chosen to be the cat, is blindfolded and placed on a chair in the middle of the circle. Put an object under the chair (students should pretend this is a piece of cheese) and signal one student in the circle to be the mouse and try to get the object under the chair without being tagged by the cat. The student trying to get the cheese scurries quietly toward the chair and the cheese, now and then making a little scratching noise to warn the cat. The cat must tag the mouse without leaving the chair. If the cat succeeds, the mouse becomes the cat and sits on the chair. If the mouse gets the cheese without being tagged, he or she may choose the next mouse, and the cat tries again.

2. Read *Night in the Country* by Cynthia Rylant and enjoy the sights and sounds of the countryside on a dark night. Or read one of the following books: *Polar Bear, Polar Bear, What Do You Hear?* by Bill Martin, Jr., *Listen to the Rain* by Bill Martin, Jr., and John Archambault, *Sounds All Around* by Jane Moncure, *The Ear Book* by Al Perkins, *Whoosh! I Hear a Sound* by Emily Hearn, *The Very Quiet Cricket* Eric Carle, or *The Five Senses: Hearing* by Rius, Puig, and Parramón. Consider recording as you read and later placing the tape in a center with the book so students can page through the book while they listen to the tape.

3. Take the class on an imaginary visit to a zoo. Make the sounds of the different animals as you walk past the cages. Stop to let students identify the animals by their sounds.

4. Center idea: make a matching game of soundmakers. In opaque containers (margarine tubs, juice containers, toilet paper rolls) place objects that make a variety of sounds. Make two of each sound for students to match.

5. Another sorting game for the listening center is Rhyme Time. Ask students (and parents) to bring in things (or miniatures of them) that rhyme. Put the items in a container and label it Rhyme Time. Students can work on auditory discrimination skills as they enjoy sorting the rhyming pairs (bag, rag; pan, fan; block, sock; pail, sail). Keep adding to the pairs to provide variety and challenge. At the center you may also wish to use the book of two-word rhymes: *One Sun: A Book of Terse Verse* by Bruce McMillan.

The Noise Song

Words and Music
by JOE WISE
(ASCAP)

LESSON 6: SENSE OF TASTE

Preparation/Materials
- Plan the food for the tasting party and contact parents to help.
- Small paper cups, plates and napkins
- Prepare chart for graphing students' likes
- Student Activities 1 & 2

Objectives
- Students will identify the mouth and tongue as body parts connected with the sense of taste.
- Students will discriminate between various types of tastes.

Lesson

1. **Circle talk.** Explain that our tongue is important to tasting. Identify different kinds of tastes: sweet, sour, salty, and bitter.

2. Have a tasting party. Provide samples of foods in each of the above categories for students to taste.

   Suggested foods:

   > sweet—raisins, grapes, jam, or honey
   > sour—lemon slices, dill pickles, grapefruit juice
   > bitter—unsweetened cocoa or chocolate
   > salty—crackers, pretzels, potato chips

   Integrate this activity with math by making a graph of the foods students liked the most. Draw simple pictures of the foods to be graphed on a chart. Have students paste a rectangle of construction paper next to the food they liked the best.

3. **Student activity.** Refer to Activities 1 and 2 in the Student Workbook. Complete the next pages of the student booklet. Students should trace the words *I can taste* in Student Activity 1 and color Student Activity 2. If time permits, ask them to draw one of their favorite foods.

4. **Closure:** "Today we talked about our sense of taste. We tasted things that are sweet, sour, bitter, and salty. Aren't you glad God made us in such a way that we can use our sense of taste to enjoy good food?"

Related Activities

- Read aloud to the class a book about the sense of taste: *A Tasting Party* by Jane Moncure, *Think about Tasting* by Henry Pluckrose, *Do You Know What I Know?* by Helen Borten, *What Do I Taste?* by Harriet Ziefert, or *The Five Senses: Taste* by Rius, Puig, and Parramón.

LESSON 7: SENSE OF TOUCH

Preparation/ Materials

- For making a set of feeling boxes:
  half gallon cardboard milk containers, six or more
  one large sock for each milk container used
  materials of varying textures—cotton balls, evergreen leaves, sand, etc.
  Cut off the toe of each sock and the top half of each milk container. Fit and then staple the cut edge of the sock over the cut edge of the container. In each feeling box put a material of a different texture.

  (Alternate option: Put the objects in a large shoe box, tape the lid shut, and cut a flap on the side for feeling.)
- Student Activities 1 & 2

Objectives

- Students will identify hands/skin as the body part associated with the sense of feeling.
- Students will discriminate among different types of materials with their sense of touch.
- Students will identify how their sense of touch helps keep them safe.

• •

Lesson

1. Explain the feeling boxes. Then pass them around, having students reach in and feel the contents of each box. Try to create an atmosphere of mystery and excitement during this activity.

   Ask students to describe the different touch sensations (soft, hard, bumpy, scratchy, prickly, smooth) and try to identify what's in each box.

2. **Circle time.** Refer to the activity about touch. Lead students to recall that we touch with our hands. Ask: "What are some things you do with your hands?" Explain that our sense of touch is related to our skin. Name or elicit from students things they can feel against their skin (a cat rubbing, a drop of rain on the cheek, warm or hot water on toes in the bath). Conclude: "Our sense of touch tells us if something is cold, warm, or hot; wet or dry; soft or smooth; soft or hard."

   Point out how our sense of touch can help keep us safe: touching sharp or hot things hurts and warns us to be careful, having cold hands or feet or ears in winter warns us that we need mittens, boots, and hats for protection.

3. **Student activity.** Refer to Activities 1 and 2 in the Student Workbook. As in previous lessons, read or sing the verse on the sheet and have students trace words as indicated in Student Activity 1. The students may color Student Activity 2

4. **Closure:** "Today we learned about our sense of touch. What part of the body do we touch with? Our sense of touch helps keep us safe. It tells us to stay away from something that's too hot or sharp. All together we have five senses: seeing, hearing, smelling, tasting, and touching."

• •

Related Activities

1. Center idea: Make a matching game with squares of materials with different textures (two or three of each texture). Use materials such as corduroy, burlap, satin or silk, and flannel. For easier handling, staple the fabrics to tagboard squares or index cards.

2. Create sculptures with natural objects of different textures. Go on a nature walk and have students collect objects such as stones, dry grass, pine cones, twigs, and leaves.

Then make sculptures by arranging and gluing the objects to small blocks of wood, styrofoam squares, or styrofoam trays covered with burlap.

3. Read books about the sense of touch: *Is It Rough? Is It Smooth? Is It Shiny?* by Tana Hoban, *Touch Will Tell* by Marcia Brown, *The Touch Book* by Jane Moncure, *My Hands* by Aliki, *The Five Senses: Touch* by Rius, Puig, and Parramón.

LESSON 8: CELEBRATING GOD'S GIFT

Preparation/Materials
- Popcorn and popcorn popper
- Student Activity page

Objectives
- Students will review the five senses.
- Students will celebrate God's gift of the senses.

• •

Lesson

1. As a culminating unit activity, pop some popcorn for the class. If possible pop it during class, so students can enjoy and help with the making and serving as well as the eating. During the activity, talk about how all the senses are working together: hearing the popping during the cooking and the crunching while eating, seeing the popcorn—before and after being popped, smelling it as it pops, touching it as we eat it, and finally, tasting it.

2. **Discussion.** Have the unit come full circle by reviewing Lesson 1 concepts: how amazing our bodies are and how by God's design all the different parts work together. Stress how important it is to take care of the senses.

3. Sing the "The Noise Song" and "God Gave Me Eyes."

4. **Student activity.** Refer to the activity page in the Student Workbook. Help students complete the last page of the unit booklets. Have them read and trace the words *Thank you, God, for my five senses.* They may enjoy making a decorative frame for the words. (You may wish to use this activity sheet as a booklet cover.) Then assemble the booklets.

5. **Closure.** Use the completed booklet for a final review.

• •

Related Activities

1. Use riddles to review body parts and senses:
   You have two of these. You can open and close them. They are often blue or brown. You can't see without them. What are they? (Eyes.)
   You have two of these on your head. You hear with them. What are they? (Ears.)
   You taste your food with this. What is it? (Tongue.)
   You can touch and pet a kitten with these. What are they? (Hands.)
   You smell popcorn popping with it. What is it? (Nose.)

2. Show a film about the five senses. *You and Your Five Senses* (Disney) is one good choice.

Unit 5

Taking Care of My Body

Goals

- Students will become aware of how their choices affect their wellness.
- Students will begin to take responsibility for making good health choices.

Background

This unit deals with basic personal health care issues—fitness, nutrition, good grooming, and dental care. The stress is on helping students become aware of the health choices they make each day, so that from a young age they begin to assume responsibility for taking care of their bodies and form healthy patterns of living. But beyond developing basic living skills and healthy habits, students need to understand *why* taking care of bodies is important.

North American society sends confusing signals to children about the value of a person's body. On one hand, there is the body cult, which makes an idol of the body. Shaping, strengthening, clothing, decorating, and gratifying the body is the central focus of some people's lives. This is a form of self-glorification and self-idolatry. On the other hand, our society also has large numbers of persons who treat their bodies carelessly, ignoring basic nutrition and physical exercise or living at a too-strenuous pace. Carried to an extreme, this view leads to self-destruction. These contrasting views, however, share an underlying attitude that says, "This is my body. And what I do with my body is my business."

Christians believe that because "we are not our own," how we treat our bodies is not an individual matter. The kingly rule of Christ extends over the body, too. The body must not become an idol, but it should be treated with respect. After all, God created the human body and breathed life into it. In fact, God charged humans to be caretakers of that creation (Genesis 1:28). As God's people we are called to care for the body and to use it in the service of God and others. How we treat bodies is important.

Vocabulary

Integrate the following suggested vocabulary:

choice(s)	grow	teeth	hot	waterproof
good	spring	rest	breakfast	shampoo
dress	fall	sleep	plant	dirt
clothes	winter	goodnight	animal	toothbrush
weather	summer	food	hair	dentist
cold	train	energy	face	explorer
exercise	dental mirror			

Unit Resources

Color Me Red! Reston, Va.: American Alliance for Health Physical Education, Recreation & Dance. An activity book (K-3) about heart health. Order from AAHPERD, 1900 Association Drive, Reston, Virginia 22091; phone 800-321-0789.

Concepts for Feeling Good. Reston, Va.: AAHPERD. A handbook for adults providing background materials for 12 important areas of wellness.

Cooper, Kenneth H. *Kid Fitness: A Complete Shape-Up Program from Birth Through High School.* New York: Bantam, 1991.

> Cooper, concerned for this "generation of unfit children," has produced a total program of diet and exercise designed "to dramatically increase overall physical fitness and self-esteem and foster healthy eating habits." A checklist of tests is included to gauge the child's level of physical health.

Fitness Discovery Activities. Reston, Va: AAHPERD.

> "A series of 55 illustrated discovery activities help both adults and children learn about fitness, nutrition, stress, body composition, smoking, and other topics."

Palmer, Hap. *Learning Basic Skills, Vol. 3.* Audiocassette. Educational Activities, Inc.

> Songs in volume 3 of this popular series include "Take a Bath," "Brush Away," and "Alice's Restaurant."

Lesson Resources

Lesson 2
Cobb, Vicki. *Getting Dressed.* New York: Harper, 1983.

Lesson 3
Walk Like the Animals. LP or audiocassette. KIMBO Educational.

K-3 Games. Basic Skills Series. Gloucester, Ont.: Canadian Association for Health, Physical Education and Recreation (CAHPER).

> This 100-page resource contains activities sequenced from simple to complex. Order from CAHPER, 1600 James Naismith Drive, Gloucester, Ontario K1B 5N4; phone 613-748-5622.

Lesson 4
Hopkins, Lee Bennett. *Still As a Star: A Book of Nighttime Poems.* Boston: Little, Brown, 1989.

Schotter, Roni. *Bunny's Night Out.* Boston: Joy Street Books, 1989.

> After a series of adventures in the dark night, Bunny discovers the delight of a warm, cozy bed.

Lessons 5-6
Barrett, Judi. *Cloudy with a Chance of Meatballs.* New York: Macmillan, 1978.

> A tale of a town where it rained food.

Food . . . Your Choice, Grade 1. Kit. Rosemont, Ill.: National Dairy Council, 1987.

> This kit contains a 40-page teacher guide, 24 food picture cards, a poster about where food comes from, and a story book. To order, contact: National Dairy Council, Nutrition Education Division, 6300 North River Road, Rosemont, Illinois 60019-9922.

Hoban, Russell. *Bread and Jam for Frances.* New York: Harper, 1964.

Raffi. *Singable Songbook.* New York: Crown, 1988.

> A popular Raffi "food song" is "Aiken Drum."

Sendak, Maurice. *Chicken Soup and Rice.* New York: Harper, 1962.

Lesson 7
Cobb, Vicki. *Keeping Clean.* New York: Harper, 1989.

Munsch, Robert. *Mud Puddle*. Toronto: Annick Press, 1982.

Prelutsky, Jack, compiler. *Read-Aloud Rhymes for the Very Young*. New York: Knopf, 1986.
"Before the Bath," "The Way They Scrub," "Happy Winter Steamy Tub," and "Naughty Soap Song" are all poems about bathing.

Lessons 8-10
American Dental Association produces a wide variety of educational materials: posters, certificates, coloring and activity books, brochures, audiovisuals, mouth models, and a K-3 curriculum (listed below). For a current catalog, write to American Dental Association, 211 East Chicago Ave., Chicago, Illinois, 60611-2678; phone 800-947-4746.

Canadian Dental Association produces kits for celebrating dental health month, posters, and a first teeth patient kit (intended for parents). To obtain a catalog, contact the Canadian Dental Association, 1815 Alta Vista Drive, Ottawa, Ontario K1G 3Y6; phone 613-523-1770. Check with local library/resource centers, which may already have these materials on file.

Bate, Lucy. *Little Rabbit's Loose Tooth*. New York: Crown, 1975.

Berenstain, Stan and Jan. *The Berenstain Bears Visit the Dentist*. New York: Random, 1983.

Brown, Marc. *Arthur's Tooth*. Boston: Little, Brown 1980.

Cooney, Nancy. *The Wobbly Tooth*. New York: Putnam, 1978.

Learning About Your Oral Health: A Prevention-Oriented School Program, Level 1. Chicago: American Dental Association, 1980.
Consists of teaching units for grades K-3, including activities and several transparencies.

Linn, Margot. *A Trip to the Dentist*. New York: Harper, 1988.

McPhail, David. *The Bear's Toothache*. Boston: Little, Brown, 1972.
A humorous story for adding a lighthearted touch to the topic of teeth.

Meet Your Teeth. Filmstrip/cassette. Disney Educational Products.
This filmstrip (seven-minute running time) explains what different types of teeth children will develop.

Rockwell, Harlow. *My Dentist*. New York: Greenwillow, 1975.

Showers, Paul. *How Many Teeth?* New York: Crowell, 1962.

Steig, William. *Doctor De Soto*. Toronto/New York: Scholastic, 1982.
A tall tale for student enjoyment.

Toothbrushing with Charlie Brown. Videocassette. Chicago: American Dental Association.
This five-minute video is one of several videos on tooth care available from the American Dental Association.

LESSON 1: CHOOSING TO BE HEALTHY

Preparation/Materials

- Puppets or other manipulatives
- Plan details of the puppet script about health choices.
- Health care items for students to identify:
  grooming items such as comb, brush, soap, toothbrush, nail clippers
  food items such as an apple or banana
  exercise/fitness items such as a jump rope, or ball
  clothing items such as hat, gloves, or boots
  optional: a specially labeled box to hold the items
- Student Activity page
- Draw circles 1 3/4" in diameter on the black paper (four per engine); precut the wheels or have students cut them out. Attach the wheels over those on the engine picture.
- Use the activity page as a model to make a large engine for a classroom health train visual.
- Optional: For making wheels for the student engines:
  black construction paper
  paper fasteners, four per engine

Objectives

- Students will recognize their own responsibility for making good health choices.
- Students will identify how various items are used to promote to good health.

Background

In this lesson students begin making a health train booklet. The booklet is an ongoing project in Units 5-7. It is completed in the last lesson of the book and is used to review health and safety concepts.

The directions for making the booklet assume that teachers will give the children one page at a time to complete, store the sheets in folders, and assemble the booklets after all the pages have been completed. However, some teachers may want to consider cutting the train cars out and assembling the booklets ahead of time.

We suggest that you use the visual in the student book to make an attractive health train visual to display in the classroom. As each new health car is introduced to the class, add a car to the visual. We suggest enlarging the train and using bright-colored construction paper to create a more striking visual. Use a 9" x 12" sheet of paper for each train car—except for the engine, which should be somewhat larger than the other cars (our model was about 11" x 15"). Enlarge the activity sheet drawings on a photocopy machine or by some other method, and use markers to add other details.

Lesson

1. Introduce the unit by talking about our responsibility to care for our bodies. Use the unit background material to place the unit in a Christian perspective.

2. To introduce the idea of making health choices, use puppets or other manipulatives to act out a day in the life of two children and the health choices they make. Consider having one make good choices and the other bad choices. Give appropriate names to the characters such as Unhealthy Hannah or Healthy Herb.

Dialogue Starter:

> Herbie (singing at the bathroom sink): I brush, brush, brush until my teeth are clean. I wash, wash, wash until the dirt's all gone. And the I comb, comb, comb my hair!
>
> Hannah: Herbie, You're wasting your time! Your teeth don't know the difference, your hands and face will just get dirty again, and your hair's going to get all messed up in no time. See? I just wipe my hands on the towel and I'm ready.
>
> Herbie: Let's see. What's for breakfast? I think I'll have orange juice, toast, and milk.
>
> Hannah: Not me. I think there's some cake left over from your birthday yesterday. Mom, can I have a piece of cake for breakfast?

Continue with a few other safety or fitness choices. Interrupt the dialogue after each segment for students to give their opinions about Herb and Hannah's health decisions. If you wish, have students ask Herbie or Hannah about their reasons for their choices.

3. Display the collection of health care items (perhaps by putting them in a special Helping Me to Be Healthy box) and have individual children choose items to identify. Ask them to explain how each is a health helper. Ask leading questions and fill in information when necessary. Do not let children take turns trying or sharing health care items because head lice and cold germs could be easily spread this way. Simply tell the children that some items should not be shared since you do not want to share germs.

4. Introduce the health project—making a health train. Show students a copy of the Student Activity or the prepared visual of the engine. Read the words printed on the engine, and explain that each car will be about something we can choose to do to help stay healthy. For a lively introduction, have students form a train (by putting hands on waist or shoulders of the student directly ahead) and chug around the room. Add a chant ("Get on the health train") to keep the chugging rhythmical.

5. **Student activity.** Refer to the activity page in the Student Workbook. Have the students color the student activity sheet and cut out the engine. If you plan to have students add black construction paper wheels, show them how to cut out the wheels and fasten them to the engine with paper fasteners. Collect the finished train cars, and store them in student folders.

6. **Closure:** "Every day we make a lot of choices. Good choices can help us stay healthy and well. In the next lessons, we're going to learn more about different ways to stay healthy."

LESSON 2: DRESSING TO STAY HEALTHY

Preparation/Materials

- For the sorting activity (step 2):
  Boys' and girls' clothing for hot, rainy, and cold weather (including seasonal hats, earmuffs, mittens, boots, shoes, bathing suits, sandals, sleeveless shirts)
  Three large signs: Hot, Cold, Rainy
- Make the first car of the classroom train visual. Add pictures to match the completed Student Activity.

- Student Activity 1 and 2. (If class has difficulty cutting, consider precutting the train cars.)

Objectives

- Students will identify types of clothing appropriate for different seasons or types of weather.
- Students will recognize wearing appropriate clothing as a way to stay healthy.

● ●

Lesson

1. Show the clothing to the class. Tell the class that clothes aren't just for show. They also help us stay healthy. Ask: "How do you think clothes help us stay healthy? (Our clothes protect our bodies in all kinds of weather.) What kind of clothes do we need in cold weather? (Warm clothes.) What kind of clothes do we need in hot weather? (Light clothes.) What kind of clothes do we need for in-between or rainy weather? (Medium weight clothes and raingear.)"

2. Together sort the clothes suitable for different kinds of weather. Put up the signs naming the categories (hot, cold, rainy) where they can be easily seen by the class. Put a bag or box of clothing in a central place. Have students take turns choosing an item from the box (possibly modeling it), deciding in which category it belongs, and explaining why. Then have them put the item under the correct sign. As the class separates the items, talk about how each helps keep us healthy. (Hats keep ears warm and body heat in, shoes protect our feet from cuts, mittens keep hands warm, and so on.)

3. Teach the following poem by A.A. Milne. Tell students it's about a child who enjoys rainy weather and the rainy weather clothes he wears. Explain the meaning of *waterproof* and *mackintosh*.

   John had great big waterproof boots on.
   John had a great big waterproof hat.
   John had a great big waterproof mackintosh.
   "And that," said John, "is that."

Students will enjoy exploring the poem's sound and rhythm. Consider having the class chant the poem or clap or stamp their feet when they come to the word *water-*

proof. Or ask the class to act out the poem while you say it and stamp their feet on the two *thats* of the last line. (Adapted from *What? Me Teach Music?* by Marjorie Lawrence [Alfred Publishing, 1982]).

4. **Student activity.** Refer to the activity pages in the Student Workbook. Have students complete train car 1 on dressing right. First, they should cut out the train car. Next, they color and cut out the clothing (along the broken lines). Then they arrange the clothing items in the correct columns in the car and glue them in place.

   Put up the health visual for the first car.

5. **Closure:** "One way to stay healthy is to dress right for the weather." Then refer to the visual to briefly sum up the lesson.

• •

Related Activities

- Center idea: mix up the clothes and put them at a center for students to sort into weather-appropriate piles.

LESSON 3: EXERCISING TO STAY HEALTHY

Preparation/Materials

- Construct car 2 of the health train visual by gluing on a completed puzzle and writing the heading "Exercise every day" with markers. (If you plan to display the car before students complete the puzzle, consider substituting pictures of children at active play for the puzzle.)
- Student Activities 1 and 2
- Optional: write the Prelutsky poem on chart paper. Draw rebus-like pictures to help students "read" the poem.
- Optional: pictures of common activities (both active and passive)

Objectives

- Students will identify different forms of exercise.
- Students will recognize that keeping active helps keep us healthy.

Background

The purpose of this lesson is to help students see the relationship between fitness and health. Students should learn that staying fit is one way to promote their overall health. Students will internalize this knowledge more easily when they understand that God wants us to be fit and that being active can be fun.

Lead students to understand, too, that exercise does not take "outside" organization. These days children often take part in youth sports from a young age, and many think that play has to be organized by the teacher or another adult. Today's children need to recapture the desire and ability for "free play," and use their own creativity to make up games and activities.

• •

Lesson

1. **Discussion.** Tell students: "One way to keep healthy is to exercise every day, to move in different ways to help your body get stronger. Your body gets stronger because exercise makes it work harder. The more you exercise, the longer you'll be able to play without getting tired." Point out that exercise can be fun. Games and sports, for example, are fun and help exercise the body. Name different common activities (or show pictures of these activities) and have students identify whether or not each involves exercise (watching TV, riding bikes, walking, running, lying down, jumping rope, sitting at the beach, swimming).

2. Give the children time to talk about their favorite active games.

3. Have students walk around the classroom imitating different animals (stretch like a cat, hop like a frog or kangaroo, walk on all fours like a dog, wriggle like a snake, waddle like a duck, and so on). Explain that all these movements are forms of exercise that develop fitness. Consider accompanying the activity with music. A recording such as "Walk Like the Animals" will add to the fun.

4. Read and enjoy the following poem by Jack Prelutsky:

   Somersaults
   It's fun turning somersaults
   and bouncing on the bed,
   I walk on my hands
   and I stand on my head.

   I swing like a monkey
   and I tumble and I shake,
   I stretch and I bend,
   but I never never break.

   I wiggle like a worm
   and I wriggle like an eel,
   I hop like a rabbit
   and I flop like a seal.

   I leap like a frog
   and I jump like a flea,
   there must be rubber
   inside of me.

   Make up actions to go with the poem. Perhaps have the class learn the poem from memory.

5. **Student activity.** Refer to Student Activities 1 and 2 in the Student Workbook. Help students complete car 2 in Student Activity 1. They should cut apart the puzzle in Student Activity 2 and assemble it to make a picture. Have them glue the picture on the train car and then color it.

   Add the second car to the health train visual.

6. **Closure:** "When we keep active and move around, we help keep our bodies healthy, too. Playing running games, swimming, riding trikes and bikes, walking are all ways to stay healthy."

• •

Related Activities

1. Have students cut pictures from magazines or newspapers of people of all ages doing fitness activities. Make a fitness bulletin board.

2. In art, have students paint or draw pictures of themselves or others doing playground activities that also develop fitness.

3. Play a game of exercise charades. Have the children take turns silently acting out their favorite exercise while the rest of the group guesses what the sport of active game is.

4. If possible, present this lesson on a gym day or when weather allows a brisk outdoor walk.

LESSON 4: RESTING TO STAY HEALTHY

Preparation/Materials
- Audio recordings of lively, rhythmic music to accompany exercise and soft, dreamy music for relaxing
- Tape recorder
- Construct car 3 of the train visual of by gluing wheels and pictures to the construction paper and writing the heading with marker.
- Student Activity page
- Optional: The day before this lesson, send home a note asking parents to allow students to bring a special bedtime friend or blanket to school.

Objectives
- Students will become aware of the relation between exercise and faster heartbeat.
- Students will recognize that sufficient rest and sleep are necessary to stay healthy.

Background
One of the hardest things to get a child to do is take a nap or go to bed for the night. Children are so full of energy that they want to be moving all the time. Naturally, they're not eager to interrupt their fun with sleep. Therefore it's difficult to get across the positive aspects of rest and sleep to this age group. Try to emphasize that we can enjoy the day much more when we have the energy to do the things we want. Being sleepy or tired keeps us from enjoying our activities.

Lesson
1. Briefly review the concept of exercise to strengthen muscles. Tell children that the heart is a muscle too. Have students place one hand over their heart to feel it beating. Hold your hand over your heart and describe its rhythm.

2. Lead students in a series of exercises to music. Do some running, skipping, and hopping. Direct the class to stop in a balanced position whenever you stop the music. Made the workout fairly strenuous.

3. Take a brief rest after the exercise and again have a heartbeat check. Can the children feel a faster heartbeat now? Stress that the exercise is strengthening the heart muscle.

4. Try some relaxation movements to a slow-moving song. Perhaps have students put their heads down on the table or have them lie down and imagine they are lying in the sand or in the grass in the warm sunshine. As they relax to the music, explain that after exercise we need rest. Talk about the need for our bodies to have sufficient rest and the importance of getting a good night's sleep in order to be ready for the next day.

5. Enjoy the following poems with the class.

Good Night, Good Night
The dark is dreaming.
Day is done.
Good night, good night
To everyone.

Good night to the birds,
And the fish in the sea,
Good night to the bears
And good night to me.
—Dennis Lee

Hushabye My Darling
Hushabye my darling
Don't you make a peep
Little creatures everywhere
Are settling down to sleep

Fishes in the millpond
Goslings in the barn
Kitten by the fireside
Baby in my arms

Listen to the raindrops
Singing you to sleep
Hushabye my darling
Don't you make a peep
—Clyde Watson

6. **Circle time.** If the children have brought stuffed animals or blankets to class, let them take turns telling about them (what they call it, how long they've had it, why they like it). Lead a discussion about what kinds of things they do to get ready for bed (brush teeth, put on pajamas, say prayers) and what helps them relax (read a book, listen to a tape, talk to an adult).

7. **Student activity.** Refer to the activity page in the Student Workbook. Students should complete train car 3 by finishing the picture. Encourage students to make a portrait of themselves at bedtime. They may show themselves in bed with their bedtime animal or getting ready for bed. Have the children fill in the rest of the page to look like their own bedroom.

8. **Closure:** "We need to exercise and keep moving, but we also need rest and sleep. That's why every night at a certain time your parents say, 'Time to go to bed.' While we're sleeping, our bodies are getting ready for the next day."

• •

Related Activities

1. Have children find out what time they go to bed each night and what time they get up. Find out how many hours most children sleep. Do their sleep patterns vary or are they very similar? Use the information for math activities.

2. Center idea: Bring in a sleeping bag or blanket, pillow, and other bedtime items. Let the children act out their bedtime rituals.

LESSON 5: FOOD FOR ENERGY AND GROWTH

Preparation/Materials

- Make a set of large food cards of typical breakfast foods such as milk, toast or bread, cereal, orange juice, egg, banana. Newspaper advertisements or actual package labels could be glued to the cards.
- Construct car 4 of the train visual by gluing pictures of healthy breakfast food to the sheet of construction paper.
- Student Activity

Objectives

- Students will identify food as a source of energy.
- Students will recognize that that they need food to grow.
- Students will become aware of the importance of eating breakfast.

Background

Although kindergartners understand in a general way that they need food, they most likely do not know exactly why they need food. This lesson introduces students to two main reasons people need food—to grow and to have energy. The lesson zeroes in on the importance of breakfast for starting the day off right by providing energy.

Lesson

1. Ask students to close their eyes and imagine they are eating their favorite food. Perhaps give volunteers opportunity to tell what their favorite food is. Tell the class that food is one of God's good gifts to us. Then ask: "Why do we eat?" Note they've already given one reason—enjoyment. Identify two other reasons: to help us grow (recall lesson of Unit 4 on growth) and to give us energy. Make the point that God made our bodies in such a way that we need food.

2. Have the class act out the start of a typical day. Perhaps have the whole class follow your movements. For example, pretend to be getting up in the morning, combing your hair, brushing your teeth, sitting down at the breakfast table, and then eating breakfast. Either narrate what's going on or pantomime and later ask the class to identify the actions. Another option is to identify each action by singing about it to the tune of "Here We Go Round the Mulberry Bush" (for example, "This is the way we comb our hair" and "This is the way we eat breakfast"). Stress that from the beginning of the day we are active, and we need food to keep going all day.

3. **Discussion.** Ask: "Why do you think we start the day by eating breakfast?" Stress that eating breakfast gives us energy and a good start to the day. Teach a few more verses to the tune of "Mulberry Bush": "Eating breakfast gives me zip," "With no breakfast I'm so slow," and "I need food for energy." Note that food also helps us grow, and add an appropriate verse: "I need food to grow up strong." Conclude by focusing on our dependence on God for our daily bread and on the fitting response—giving thanks to God.

4. Set up the food cards so that all can see them. Have students identify the foods and name the ones they usually eat for breakfast. As they pick out the foods, comment on how the food will keep them healthy (for example, "Milk helps your bones and teeth"). Optional: integrate a math activity using the food as category headings to graph what the students ate for breakfast that morning.

5. **Student activity.** Refer to the activity page in the Student Workbook with car 4 of the train. Students should cut out the car and draw a picture of breakfast foods or of themselves eating breakfast.

   Add car 4 to the health train visual.

6. **Closure:** "Today we talked about why we need food. We learned that we all need food to grow and to give us energy. Eating breakfast starts the day out right and gives us energy to run and play and think in school. We'll be talking more about food together later."

• •

Related Activities

- Teach students the Raffi song "Aiken Drum." Sing all the verses and then have the class draw pictures of Aiken Drum (with hair of spaghetti, eyes of meatballs, nose of cheese, mouth of pizza). Make up verses for other body parts to complete the picture.

LESSON 6: PLANT OR ANIMAL?

Preparation/Materials

- For making a chart similar to the Student Activity:

  large piece of tagboard (or use the bulletin board)

  tacks or tape

  two large cards for chart headings—*Foods from plants* and *Foods from animals*

  A set of 10 large cards to place on the chart. Prepare the cards by drawing/coloring pictures on them to correspond with food pictures on the Student Activity.
- Songs celebrating God's gift of food
- Student Activities 1 and 2
- Optional: plan for students to make nutritious classroom snacks. See step 6 for suggestions.

Objectives

- Students will know that foods come from both plants and animals.

- Students will identify foods according to their sources.
- Students will recognize that it is healthy to eat a wide variety of foods.

Background

At this grade level, students learn that all foods have two sources, plant and animal. Learning this simple classification lays the groundwork for understanding food groups (taught in grade 1 of this curriculum) and the reason why eating from all groups is necessary for a balanced diet. In this lesson stress the importance of eating a wide variety of foods and encourage students to taste unfamiliar foods.

The idea for this lesson is adapted from *Food . . . Helps Me Grow,* published by the National Dairy Council.

• •

Lesson

1. Review previous lesson concepts. Ask: "Why do we need food?" (To help us grow and give us energy.) Explain that we also need to eat many different kinds of food to keep us healthy. Some foods come from animals and some come from plants, and we need both. This lesson will help students discover which foods are from plants and which from animals.

2. Display the chart. Attach the headings *Foods from plants* and *Foods from animals.* Explain the titles and teach new vocabulary.

3. **Student activity.** Refer to Student Activities 1 and 2 in the Student Workbook. Point out that the titles in Student Activity 1 correspond to those on the chart. Ask class members to cut apart the food pictures in Student Activity 2.

   Then work with the class to identify the plant and animal sources of the various foods in the picture. Consider beginning with plant sources. Suggested procedure to follow:

hold up a picture card and ask students to identify what it is and whether it's a plant or animal. (Ask questions about how the plant grows to help with the identification—on a tree, under the ground, and so on.) Then put the card in the proper column on the chart and give students time to put their corresponding picture in the correct column on Activity Sheet 1. Follow the same procedure with foods from animals. Be sure students get the connection of eggs and chickens and milk and cheese and cows.

Have students glue their pictures in place. Or, if you wish, ask them to scramble their pictures and then to work independently to classify them into plant and animal foods before finally gluing the pictures to the page.

4. Optional: prepare nutritious snacks. Let the students help with the preparation as much as possible. Here are a few suggestions:
      celery filled with cheese and topped with raisins
      pieces of fruit that students can cut (bananas are good) with their choice of topping
          (granola, coconut, nuts)
      fresh vegetables (carrots, cauliflower) and yogurt dip
      orange juice (making freshly-squeezed juice is too time consuming, but cut a few or-
          anges crosswise and let students squeeze out some juice to make the source
          clear)

5. Sing songs that celebrate God's good gifts, especially the gift of food. Suggestions: "Praise and Thanksgiving" (*Psalter Hymnal,* 631), "To God Who Gives Us Daily Bread," and "For Health and Strength" (*Children's Hymnbook,* 50 and 51).

6. **Closure:** "We learned today that some foods come from animals and some from plants. (Perhaps have students name foods from each category.) Food is one of the many good gifts of God. When we pray before we eat, we thank God for giving us the food."

• •

Related Activities

1. Provide more pictures of food (only of those foods whose source is easy for students to determine) at a center and two boxes for sorting them into plant and animal categories.

2. Integrate with language arts by enjoying stories about food. Suggestions: *Cloudy with a Chance of Meatballs* by Judi Barrett, *Chicken Soup and Rice* by Sendak, *Bread and Jam for Frances* by Russell Hoban.

3. Visit a supermarket to see the wide variety of foods available and identify whether the food sources are plant or animal.

LESSON 7: PERSONAL GROOMING

Preparation/Materials

- Student Activities 1a & 1b. Students will tape the two sheets together to make the visual. Consider mounting it on tagboard or construction paper and coloring it.
- Dolls and grooming materials for practicing good grooming
- Student Activity 2. Make the train visual, car 5. Glue a tissue or a small piece of terry cloth and a picture/ wrapper of soap on the construction paper. Use a marker to write the caption and draw a picture of the toothpaste, toothbrush, and comb.
- Items to glue on the activity sheet:
  pastel tissue or small piece of terry cloth, one per student
  soap wrapper (cut down) or picture of soap, one per student

Objectives

- Students will connect being clean with being healthy.
- Students will identify specific ways to keep clean.
- Students will practice good grooming techniques by playing with dolls.

Background

The origin of health education is personal health. In the early years of school health programs, personal health was the entire curriculum. However, more recently the trend has been to de-emphasize personal health. One reason is that most of the major contagious illnesses associated with personal health habits have either been eradicated or controlled.

However, this trend to de-emphasize personal health as a topic is unfortunate. Take the mundane area of dental health, for example. Fully 97% of the students in our schools will have some kind of dental problems in their lifetime. Or take the topic of cleanliness. Reminders about daily personal health habits may seem to be a form of parental or teacher nagging, but students do need to be reminded that they can spread germs when they do not wash their hands before they eat or after they use the bathroom. Stress the positive side of personal health. Grooming habits such as bathing and brushing teeth will help students stay healthy and clean and be more attractive. And they will like themselves better when they are healthy and clean.

Lesson

1. Refer to Student Activities 1a and 1b in the Student Workbook. Students may cut on the dotted lines and tape the two halves of the visual together, then color it. Use the poster to talk with the class about grooming habits:

   Hair: wash with shampoo to get out the dirt and grease. Then dry and comb it.

   Face: wash with soap and water.

   Teeth: brush at least twice a day (go into details later).

   Hands: Lather up with soap and water before eating, after using the toilet, and whenever they're dirty. Scrub fingernails with a brush. Try not to bite nails because then dirt gets into the mouth.

   Whole body: Shower or bathe frequently. Bathing removes dirt and some germs that can make us sick.

Stress that good grooming helps us look good, feel good, and keep healthy.

2. Have children practice good grooming techniques on dolls in a center. If possible, let them shampoo and rinse dolls' hair in basins, etc. If the classroom has a sink, let students take turns demonstrating good handwashing—with soap. Give some reward for a job well done.

3. **Student activity.** Refer to Student Activity 2 in the Student Workbook. Help students complete the cleanliness car. Have them color the comb, toothbrush, and toothpaste and then paste the tissue or terry cloth and soap wrapper/picture on the car.

   Add the prepared car to the health train visual.

4. **Closure:** "Keeping our hands and nails and hair and face and teeth—in fact, our whole body—clean helps us stay healthy. Name some things we use to scrub and clean ourselves."

LESSON 8: TWO SETS OF TEETH

Preparation/Materials

- Small mirrors, one for every pair or group of students
- Student Activity page showing stages of replacement of primary tooth
- Book to read aloud about losing primary teeth
- Optional: bottle of baby food

Objectives

- Students will identify the purpose of teeth.
- Students will understand the sequence of primary/secondary teeth.

Background

This lesson explains the process of eruption and shedding of primary teeth. The American Dental Association's program Learning About Your Oral Health states that the process begins at about age 6 and is complete by 12-13 years (except for third permanent molars, which erupt at 17-21). There are 20 primary teeth (8 incisors, 4 cuspids, and 8 molars), but there are 32 permanent teeth (8 incisors, 4 cuspids, 8 bicuspids, and 12 molars). Stress that care of primary teeth is important because they guide the position of the permanent teeth.

• •

Lesson

1. Explain the purpose of our teeth. Give children small mirrors and have them smile and take a good look at their teeth. Ask: Why do you think God made us so that we have teeth? What are our teeth for? (They give us a nice smile, but primarily so that we can chew our food.) We bite into our food with our front teeth and then we grind up our food with our back teeth. You may also wish to explain that teeth help us talk. Children can observe this by looking in the mirrors as they make s or th sounds.

2. **Discussion.** Lead students to recall that newborn babies don't have teeth; they can only drink milk or juice. Later they eat mashed food. (Perhaps bring in a jar of baby food to demonstrate.) Explain that children gradually get their first set of teeth, called baby teeth or primary teeth. When children are about six years old, they get their second set of teeth, permanent teeth that they'll keep their whole life. Stress that taking care of the first set of teeth is important because these teeth keep a space open for the permanent teeth.

   Refer to the activity page in the Student Workbook showing how the primary tooth is replaced by the emerging secondary tooth. Note how the roots of the primary tooth gradually disappear. Tell students that this is why the primary tooth became looser and looser. The whole process of replacing a tooth takes about one year.

3. Read one of the delightful children's stories about losing primary teeth. Suggestions: *Little Rabbit's Loose Tooth* by Lucy Bate, *The Wobbly Tooth* by Nancy Cooney, *Arthur's Tooth* by Marc Brown.

4. **Closure:** "Today we talked about teeth. We need our teeth to give us nice smiles, to talk, and to eat. We start getting teeth when we are babies (called our primary teeth), but when we're about six years old, these teeth gradually come out and we get a second set of teeth. If we take good care of our teeth, we'll have them for years and years and years—for as long as we need them."

LESSON 9: TAKING CARE OF TEETH

Preparation/Materials

- Toothbrush and comb for demonstrating brushing techniques
- Student Activity page. You may wish to pre-cut the puppets and finger holes.
- Optional: chart paper
- Optional: Song "Brushing Away" by Hap Palmer from the audiocassette *Learning Through Music, Health and Safety, vol. 3* and cassette player

Objectives

- Students will identify two ways to keep teeth healthy.
- Students will recall that brushing teeth regularly can help prevent cavities.
- Students will be able to describe how to brush teeth.

Background

"Oral disease is one of the most prevalent health problems in America today. It is the exceptional person who possesses a full complement of 32 teeth, none of which is either filled or decayed. Statistics reveal that by the time the average child is 6 years old, three primary teeth have been attacked by decay at least one. By age 21, the average young adult has 11 decayed, missing or filled teeth." This statement in the forward of the American Dental Association's *Learning about Your Oral Health: Level 1* stresses how important it is to educate children about dental care. By instilling a positive attitude toward oral health practices at an early age, teachers can help motivate students to establish good health practices.

We suggest you contact your local dentist or dentists' association for information about current toothbrushing techniques. The association may also have posters or materials available. Or contact your national Dental Association for plaque control kits and other helpful materials.

• •

Lesson

1. Ask: "What can we do to keep our teeth healthy?" (Brush them and eat good food.)

   Explain that brushing teeth regularly helps us to avoid getting *cavities*. Briefly explain that cavities are tiny holes in our teeth caused by food left on the teeth and by germs.

2. Demonstrate how to brush teeth in order to cover all surfaces. (Use current toothbrushing techniques: usually small circles at this age.) Stress that brushing teeth should be done at least twice a day—in the morning and at night. It's also good to brush after sweet or sticky snacks. Consider making a sequence chart with the class to illustrate the steps in brushing teeth. Display the chart in the classroom.

3. To reinforce the importance of brushing, sing a song about it. Make up a piggyback song to the tune of "Are You Sleeping?"

Brush your teeth.
Brush your teeth.
Yes, I will,
Yes, I will.
Brush them twice a day,
Brush them twice a day.
Every day,
Every day.

You can sing this as an echo song, with the teacher singing the first line and the students repeating on the second.

Or sing the song "Brushing Away" by Hap Palmer, or play it while students work on their activity.

4. **Student activity.** Refer to the activity page in the Student Workbook. Students should first color and then cut out the finger puppets. They most likely will need help making the finger holes. Show the students how to fold the flap and insert their fingers. Give class members time to enjoy playing with the puppets—brushing the tooth with the toothbrush.

5. **Closure:** "What are cavities? What are two ways to help keep our teeth healthy?" (Eating healthy food and brushing teeth.)

Related Activities

1. Have the children make their own tooth powder. Draw pictures to illustrate the steps of the following recipe. Combine: 1 tablespoon of salt, 2 tablespoons of baking powder, and a little peppermint flavoring. Have the children place the ingredients, in order, into a small container such as a baby food jar and mix them. Give students a copy of the recipe and of the instructions to take home with a sample of the tooth powder. (Instructions: To use, wet the toothbrush and put some of the powder on the bristles.)

2. For an art activity make large mouth shapes on red construction paper. Tint school glue pink with food coloring. The children can draw in the gum line with the glue. White popcorn seeds can be placed into the glue as teeth.

3. Paint with dental floss and toothbrushes. Show the students how to dip the dental floss into paint and drag it across the paper. The toothbrushes can be used to brush or spatter paint. Encourage the children to experiment!

(These three ideas are from *Teaching Young Children Using Themes* [Good Year Books, 1991].)

LESSON 10: GETTING DENTAL CHECKUPS

Preparation/Materials

- Book about dental checkup to read aloud
- Materials for roleplaying a visit to the dentist
- Optional: ask a local dentist to furnish an old dental mirror and explorer, or draw enlargements of the sketches on tagboard:

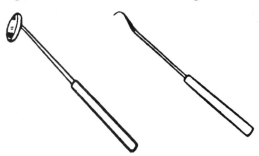

Objectives

- Students will recognize the importance of dental checkups.
- Students will be able to identify two basic dental tools.

Background

Because dental cavities may begin as soon as children have teeth, children should have their first dental examination before all of the primary teeth have erupted (around the age of two). However, it is very likely that some kindergartners will not have been to the dentist yet. Use this lesson to explain who dentists are and what dental checkups are all about.

Lesson

1. Talk about the importance of dental checkups. Note that in spite of brushing and healthy diet, sometimes cavities do form. The dentist can fill any cavity or little hole so that it doesn't get any bigger.

2. Explain what the dentist will do: shine a light into the mouth and check each tooth for cavities. Show the two dental tools, an explorer and dental mirror, or draw sketches of the tools on the board. Ask students what the tools are for. Explain that the dentist looks into the mouth and uses an explorer and dental mirror to help find any the little holes (too small for children to see by looking in their mouths).

3. Read a story about a visit to the dentist. *The Berenstain Bears Visit the Dentist* by Stan and Jan Berenstain, *A Trip to the Dentist* by Margot Linn, and *My Dentist* by Harlow Rockwell are a few suggested titles.

4. Have students roleplay visiting the dentist. Assign the roles of dentist, dental hygienist, and patient to several students in the class. Use props such as aprons, a gown, and a chair. Consider having one student roleplay a patient who does not like to go the dentist, and follow with a student who shows a cooperative attitude.

5. **Closure:** "To take care of our teeth we eat good food and we brush our teeth twice a day. But there's one more thing we can do. We can go to the dentist for a checkup. The

dentist will look in our mouth with an explorer. If we have any cavities, the dentist will fix them, so that they don't get any bigger."

6. Review the unit concepts with the classroom health train.

● ●

Related Activities

1. Invite a dentist or dental hygienist to visit the classroom and talk about dental check-ups.

2. For a touch of humor and integration with language arts read these tall tales about teeth: *The Bear's Toothache* by David McPhail or *Doctor De Soto* by William Steig.

3. If you have been able to obtain old dental tools, set up a station for the children to experiment with a mirror, a small flashlight and a looking box. You will need a covered box, tape, stickers and colored paper or markers. Attach stickers inside the box after cutting a hole at one end. Tape the cover on the box. Make a mouth by coloring or cutting paper to glue around the outside of the cut hole. The children can use the mirror and flashlight to look inside the box and count how many stickers they find. Or, make matching sticker cards and have the children find the sticker in the box that matches the card they have drawn from the pile.

4. Make "teeth" with the children by mixing plaster of Paris and pouring it into egg cartons, filling each individual section to the top. When they have completely hardened, pop the teeth out and give each student a tooth or pair of teeth. Discuss ways dentists drill and scrape teeth. Children may pretend to be dentists, drilling their "tooth" with toothpicks or craft sticks and filling with modeling clay.

(Suggestions 3 and 4 are adapted from *Teaching Young Children Using Themes* [Good Year Books, 1991].)

Unit 6

Being Safe

Goals

- Students will become safety conscious.
- Students will develop skills for protecting themselves.

Background

This unit covers several basic safety issues—traffic safety, fire safety, and stranger and child abuse education. The first two are straightforward safety issues. We all recognize that children must be aware of potential traffic and fire hazards and need to develop skills to protect themselves. But the last two areas—stranger and child abuse education—are also basic safety issues, and students need help in those areas also. As much as we would like young children to remain innocent, in order to protect children we must deal with the reality of danger and of sinful acts such as child abuse. Of course, it's important to take a balanced approach. Students must be informed, but not unnecessarily frightened. Be matter-of-fact, and encourage them to develop self-confidence in dealing with all these issues.

Vocabulary

Integrate the following suggested vocabulary:

rules	go	drop	listen
street	emergency	roll	smoke
traffic	telephone	touch	safe
fire	number	crawl	private parts
stop	stop light		

Unit Resources

Davis, Diane. *Something Is Wrong At My House: A Book About Parent's Fighting*. Seattle: Parenting Press, 1984.

Winston-Hillier, Randy. *Some Secrets Are for Sharing*. Denver: MAC, 1986.
>Both of these books deal with domestic violence. Davis's book addresses the problem of violent parental fights; Winston-Hillier's book addresses the problem of emotional and physical abuse of a child by a parent. These problems are not covered in the health program, but teachers may wish to use these resources one-on-one with students living with family violence.

KidsRights is a comprehensive distributor for materials on personal safety issues. For a catalog, contact KidsRights, 3700 Progress Boulevard, Mount Dora, Florida, 32757; phone 800-892-KIDS.

Lesson Resources

Lesson 2

AAA offers a variety of traffic safety materials. One item of interest is a series of six single-concept cartoon films for primary grade level, which use Otto the Auto to teach basic pedestrian, car passenger, and bicycle safety. Contact the local AAA office for a catalog or write to AAA Foundation for Traffic Safety, 1730 M Street, N.W., Suite 401, Washington, D.C. 20036; phone 202-775-1456.

Blakely, Cindy, and Suzanne Drinkwater. *The Look Out! Book: A Child's Guide to Street Safety.* Toronto/New York: Scholastic, 1986.
> Too difficult for kindergarten level, but still helpful as a teacher resource.

Bucklebear Team's Traffic Safety Series. Okemos, Mich.: Shinn.
> A wide variety of materials, all with a bear theme—teacher guides, videos, activity and coloring books, and posters. For a catalog, contact Shinn & Associates, 2853 W. Jolly, Okemos, Michigan 48865; phone 517-332-0211.

Chlad, Dorothy. *When I Cross the Street.* Chicago: Childrens Press, 1982.
> Alerts children to signals, signs, and traffic patterns.

Hall, Barbara and Doug. *Playing It Safe: Home, Summer, and Winter Street Smart Activities for Children.* Willowdale, Ont.: Firefly Books, 1990.
> Endorsed by the Block Parent Program of Canada, this activity book (intended for ages 5-10) illustrates a variety of safety rules. Pages are reproducible for classroom instruction.

Hoban, Tana. *I Read Signs.* New York: Mulberry Books, 1983.
> Large photographs of signs.

Leaf, Munro. *Safety Can Be Fun.* New York: Harper, 1988.
> This reprint of an "oldie" covers basic traffic safety.

Petty, Kate. *Stop, Look and Listen, Mr. Toad.* Toronto/New York: Barron's, 1991.
> Mr. Toad and his growing family learn how to cross the street safely. Not great literature, but the story gets the safety message across in an amusing way.

Lesson 3

Chlad, Dorothy. *Strangers.* Chicago: Childrens Press, 1982.

Berenstain, Stan and Jan. *The Berenstain Bears Learn About Strangers.* New York: Random, 1985.

Fulton, Ginger A. *Saying NO to Mr. Stranger.* Chicago: Moody Press, 1987.
> The book, for ages 3-6, heavily emphasizes obeying parents as God's appointed caregivers and in particular obeying parents' rule to not go anywhere with a stranger. It defines strangers and presents situations for practicing saying no to a stranger.

Girard, Linda Walvoord. *Who Is a Stranger and What Should I Do?* Niles, Ill.: Whitman, 1985.

Holland, M., and J. Demers. *How Do You Know Who's a Stranger?* Pinellas Park, Fla.: Willowisp, 1987.

Lessons 4-5

Chlad, Dorothy. *Matches, Lighters, and Firecrackers Are Not Toys.* Chicago: Childrens Press, 1982.

Hamkin, Rebecca. *I Can Be a Firefighter.* Chicago: Childrens Press, 1985.
> Describes firefighting, rescue work, fire prevention, and paramedic rescue.

Hanum, Dotti. *A Visit to the Fire Station.* Chicago: Childrens Press, 1985.

Learn Not to Burn Curriculum: A Fire Prevention and Safety Education Program for School Children, Level 1. Third edition. Quincy, Mass.: National Fire Protection Association, 1987.
> Contains 22 lesson plans, lists of teaching aids, and fire safety information for teachers. This

program is being used in both Canadian and U.S. schools. For ordering address see the NFPA entry below.

Matches Aren't for Children. 16 slides. Fire Protection Publications.
Intended for preschool and K, this resource stresses the dangers of matches. Available from Oklahoma State University, Stillwater, Oklahoma 74074.

My Book About Phoning for Help. South Deerfield, Mass.: Channing L. Bete.
Channing L. Bete produces a variety of coloring and activity books on safety topics. Titles include *No Smoking, School Bus Safety,* and *About Traffic Safety.* To obtain copies of the booklets or a catalog, contact the publisher: 200 State Rd., South Deerfield, Massachusetts 01373-0200; phone 800-628-7733.

The National Fire Protection Association has a wealth of materials available: videos and filmstrips, activity and coloring books, posters, and stickers. For a catalog, contact the association at 1 Batterymarch Park, Quincy, Massachusetts 02269-9101; phone 800-344-3555.

Rey, Margaret. *Curious George Visits the Fire Station.* Boston: Houghton, 1988.
Available in a book/audiocassette packet.

What Do I Do When I See a Fire? 13-minute film. Quincy, Mass.: National Fire Protection Agency.
Puppets teach about how to report a fire.

Lesson 7
Bahr, Amy. *It's Okay to Say No.* New York: Grosset & Dunlap, 1986.

C.A.R.E. Kit: A Sexual Abuse Prevention Program for Children Aged 5-9. Surrey, B.C.: Child Abuse Education Productions Association.
A comprehensive, but rather costly resource, which includes a teacher guide with lesson plans, visuals for presenting key ideas, audiocassette and student book, and puppets. Write to the publisher: P.O. Box 183, Surrey, British Columbia V3T 4W8; phone 604-581-5116.

Carl, Angela R. *Good Hugs and Bad Hugs.* Cincinnati, Ohio: Standard, 1985.
This activity book is a helpful teacher resource providing activities for reinforcing or expanding lesson ideas. Written from a Christian perspective, the level of individual activities varies considerably.

Colao, Flora, and Tamar Hosansky. *Your Children Should Know.* New York: Harper, 1983.
Provides background information on the reasons for abuse and ways to prevent abuse.

Dayee, Frances S. *Private Zone.* New York: Warner Books, 1982.
A read-together book about appropriate/inappropriate touching. It avoids naming anatomical parts and instead uses the term "private zone." It defines the private zone as special parts of the body covered by a bathing suit. Simple and clear presentation of basics for preventing sexual abuse.

De Moor, Ary, and others. *Child Abuse Education.* Part 3 of *Now You Are the Body of Christ: A Family Life Education Program for Christian Schools.* Edmonton: CSI District 11 Association and Grand Rapids: Christian Schools International, 1989.
Developed by the Curriculum Coordinator and five teachers of CSI District 11, this is a curriculum outline for teaching abuse prevention in kindergarten through grade 12. This valuable resource includes a sample protocol for reporting sexual abuse. Order from District 11

Curriculum Office, The King's College, 10766 - 97th St., Edmonton, Alberta T5H 2M1 or from Christian Schools International.

Freeman, Lory. *It's My Body.* Seattle: Parenting Press, 1982.
Intended to help children ages 3-6 identify uncomfortable touch and to give them the language to deal with "unwanted touching of any kind."

Girard, Linda Walvoord. *My Body Is Private.* Niles, Ill.: Whitman, 1984.
Sensitively written book covering types of touches, how to deal with disturbing situations, and telling adults about inappropriate touch. Ages 5-8.

Jance, Judith. *It's Not Your Fault.* Children's Safety Series. Edmonds, Wash.: Charles Franklin Press, 1985.
Including a read-aloud section, discussion questions, and background information, Jance's helpful book has two purposes: to assure children who have been sexually abused that they are not responsible and to teach all children the basics of preventing sexual abuse. The read-aloud story is about Terry and how she comes to tell adults about the sexual abuse of her step-grandfather. For ages 6-10.

Kehoe, Patricia. *Something Happened and I'm Scared to Tell: A Book for Young Victims of Abuse.* Seattle: Parenting Press, 1987.
Intended for the young child who is a suspected victim of sexual or physical abuse, this 26-page booklet is designed to encourage victims to speak out. Summary: in conversation with a kind lion, a child tells about being abused. The lion encourages the child to tell the truth and keep telling the truth until somebody listens, names people who may be abusers (including some family members), defines sexual abuse (naming genitals—vagina, penis, and anus), and helps the child recognize and deal with confused feelings. A direct, honest, and supportive approach.

Kraizer, Sherryll Kerns. *The Safe Child Book.* New York: Delacorte, 1985.
This book is intended for parents, but teachers will also find it helpful because of its concrete approach to preventing sexual abuse of children.

Lenett, Robin, and Dana Barthelme. *Sometimes It's O.K. to Tell Secrets! A Parent/Child Manual for the Protection of Children.* New York: Tom Doherty Associates, 1986.
Helpful for teachers as well as parents, this resource devotes five chapters to educating adults about the dangers and consequences of sexual abuse and about the importance of breaking the "barrier of silence" that surrounds abuse. Chapter 6 contains about 25 story situations which end with the question, What would you do? Although the material is above the kindergarten level, teachers will find ideas which they can adapt.

Murphy, Elspeth. *Sometimes I Need to Be Hugged.* Weston, Ont./Elgin, Ill.: Cook, 1981.
A paraphrase of Psalm 84 for children.

Plummer, Carol A. *Preventing Sexual Abuse: Activities and Strategies for Those Working with Children and Adolescents.* Holmes Beach, Fla.: Learning Publications, 1984.
Contains a skeleton outline of programs to prevent sexual abuse in K-6, 7-12, and programs for developmentally disabled persons. Other features: suggestions for setting up a prevention program and for involving parents, guidelines for instructors, and curriculum guides. A

helpful teacher resource, but be aware that suggested roleplay situations require careful evaluation. Order from the publisher: P.O. Box 1326, Holmes Beach, Florida 33509.

Sanford, Doris. *I Can't Talk About It.* Portland, Ore.: Multnomah Press, 1986.
Annie, a child who is being sexually abused by her father, talks with God about her pain. Two noteworthy aspects: its sensitivity to abused children's tendency to blame themselves and its stress on the need for forgiveness. Not suitable to read in its entirety in the classroom, but the book may be helpful for approaching a child who has been abused.

Talking About Touching Early Childhood Kit. Seattle: Committee for Children.
Intended for preschool-kindergarten, this kit is costly, but includes laminated lessons, teacher guide, a parent guide, flannelboard characters, a filmstrip-in-video, and a story booklet with audio tape. For information about this or a catalog of other materials, contact Committee for Children, 172 - 20th Ave., Seattle, Washington 98122-5862; phone 800-634-4449.

LESSON 1: ALL ABOUT RULES

Preparation/Materials
- Chart paper
- Student Activities 1 & 2

Objectives
- Students will be able to describe why rules are necessary.
- Students will identify the connection between rules and loving our neighbor.
- Students will identify common school safety rules.

Background

Often children are taught safety from a purely negative point of view. And they often conclude that safety rules are something that prevent them from having fun or doing what they want to do. Children need to understand that rules are helpers and not hindrances. Rather than a list of arbitrary laws, safety rules are guidelines helping us to stay well and healthy. And since what we do affects others, rules are necessary for the welfare of the entire community.

Young children in particular need safety education because they often act impulsively and without thinking about their safety or the safety of others. Children playing on the playground are absorbed in play. They take the shortest route to their destination, even if it means running right behind moving swings. If a ball goes into the street, their first reaction is to dart out to get the ball in order to quickly resume playing. So safety education needs to be started when children are young and repeated at each primary grade level.

● ●

Lesson

1. **Discussion.** Introduce the lesson topic, safety rules, with a personal anecdote. Tell about something you wanted to do when you were a child but couldn't because your parents (or school) forbade it. Describe what rule you were expected to obey. For example, perhaps you wanted to play ball in the street. Lead students to understand that rules help to keep them healthy and safe. Use the following questions to get children thinking about purpose of rules:

   "Who do you think made the rule?"

   "Why do you think they made the rule?"

   "What do you think might have happened if I broke the rule?"

Give the children some more examples of common rules that they follow. Ask for volunteers to answer what might happen to them if they break or forget the rule. Lead the children to recognize that rules help them to be safe.

Take the discussion a step further. Tie in obeying rules with loving our neighbor, being considerate of others. What happens when we run and knock others over, litter, or don't return library books? Rules are for students' own safety and also for the safety and enjoyment of others.

2. Work with students to develop an experience chart of rules that help students to stay safe at school. Some rules to cover:
   - Walk—don't run—in the halls and on steps.
   - Put away things that others could trip over.
   - Use playground equipment carefully—take turns on slides or other equipment.
   - Walk in safe areas when near swings.
   - Use balls and other equipment in designated areas.
   - Carry sharp objects point down.

   Make simple sketches on the chart to help students identify each rule. Talk about what would happen if we didn't have the rule. You may wish to cut out any rules from the chart that apply to your classroom and display them in appropriate areas as reminders.

3. **Student activity.** Refer to Student Activities 1 and 2 in the Student Workbook. Look at the pictures in Student Activity 1 with the students and have them identify the safety rules being broken. Then have students cut apart the pictures in Student Activity 2 showing rules being obeyed. Then direct them to paste the picture of the rule being followed over the one showing the same rule being broken. Finally, have students read the sentence at bottom of the page and have students finish it by tracing the word *safe.*

4. **Closure:** "God wants us to be safe. He gives us parents and other helpers that make rules to help us be safe. And God makes us able to choose to follow rules that will help keep us safe."

• •

Related Activities

1. In centers students can use dolls or other manipulatives to act out the situations shown on the lesson activity sheet.

2. Demonstrate what happens when people don't follow rules. Explain the rules of a game and then play it with the class. But then let children ignore the rules. Stop when they realize what bedlam results from ignoring rules. Make the point: even games need rules to be fun.

LESSON 2: SAFETY ON THE STREET

Preparation/Materials

- Student Activity pages 1–5
- Make a set of traffic signs out of heavy paper or tagboard.
- Construct car 6 for the health train visual by fastening traffic safety pictures to the piece of construction paper. Write the caption "Follow safety rules" with a marker.
- Optional: use masking tape to mark out street blocks and crosswalks in the class-room, in the gymnasium, or in another available large space.
- Optional: ask older students to assist (see step 3)

Objectives

- Students will learn basic pedestrian rules.
- Students will apply the rules to specific situations.

Lesson

1. Talk about basic pedestrian rules:
   - Walk on the sidewalk or grass away from the curb. (Warn about cars entering or backing out of driveways.)
   - Cross the street at the corner. Stay in the crosswalk, if there is one.
   - Look all ways and listen for cars before crossing. (Warn about turning cars.)
   - Walk, don't run across the street.

   Stress that making the choice to obey these rules helps keep us safe.

2. Use Student Activity pages 1–4 to teach the children the following song to the tune of "The Wheels on the Bus."

   > When we're going for a walk,
   > we stay on the sidewalk,
   > stay on the sidewalk,
   > stay on the sidewalk.
   > When we're going for a walk,
   > we stay on the sidewalk
   > all around the town.

   > Subsequent verses:
   > When we're going for a walk
   > we stop at the corner…
   > we look both ways…
   > we stay in the crosswalk…

3. Go for a walk to illustrate what safety choices students must make. If you prefer, practice pedestrian safety in the gymnasium or on the playground. Use masking tape or chalk to mark out street blocks and crosswalks. Perhaps have some older students be

the cars. During the activity, review/teach the meaning of traffic lights and and common traffic signs with the teacher-prepared traffic signs. If pedestrian crosswalk lights are in use at intersections in your area, teach students how to read and activate the lights. As you walk, sing the "When We're Going for a Walk" song!

4. **Student activity.** Refer to the activity page in the Student Workbook. Have students complete Student Activity 5. Discuss the pictures and and review the meaning of a traffic stoplight and a stop sign. Note the color words on the traffic light. Have students color the pictures.

   Show students the corresponding train car visual and add it to the classroom health train.

5. **Closure:** "Today we learned ways to stay safe on the streets. We learned to look out for cars and to cross streets safely. In the next lesson we'll be learning more about safety."

• •

Related Activities

1. Center idea: lay out street blocks with masking tape on a table or large piece of cardboard and have students practice the safety rules with manipulatives.

2. Invite a police officer to talk about pedestrian safety. Some police departments have developed high interest presentations.

3. Focus on bus safety. After a brief talk by a school bus driver, have students go to the school bus to practice bus safety rules. If this is not feasible, practice bus safety rules in the classroom. Set up chairs to simulate bus seats. Then roleplay a school bus ride (include boarding the bus, taking seats, riding on the bus, and exiting).

4. Reinforce safety ideas by reading a book such as Dorothy Chlad's *When I Cross the Street*.

LESSON 3: STRANGER EDUCATION

Preparation/Materials
- Book to read aloud about safety and strangers
- Optional: puppets

Objectives
- Students will be able to identify strangers.
- Students will learn safety rules for dealing with strangers.

Background

Christians speak of having child-like faith—that is, of believing without questioning. Children are known for their trust and confidence in adults around them. Unfortunately, it is this quality that may bring children into grave danger with some adults.

It is very difficult to help young children tell the difference between kind, helpful strangers and strangers who wish to hurt them. But for their safety, children need to learn who strangers are and how to be safe around strangers. These rules need to be repeated so that the children become very familiar with them. Keep the discussion low key to avoid frightening the class members. Assure them that most strangers are friendly and helpful and that it's not likely they'll be harmed by strangers. Compare stranger education to fire safety education: fire isn't very common, but being prepared to deal with a fire helps to keep them safe.

Make parents aware of the material covered in this lesson. Encourage them to reinforce the content by talking to their children about any special family rules about strangers. For example, what are family rules about telephone conversations with strangers and about answering the door at home?

Lesson

1. Briefly review street safety rules. Then introduce the topic of stranger education. Talk about the importance of always having parents' permission before accepting rides or going along with a someone. Teach the meaning of the word *stranger* ("a person that you don't know"). Point out that even if someone talks in a friendly way, if the child doesn't know that person, he or she is a stranger.

   Teach the basic rule: Never go for a ride or a walk with a stranger.

2. To make the topic more concrete, give several examples of plausible requests or an invitation a stranger might make. Have the students practice saying no after each. Consider using puppets to dramatize the situations.

   Examples:
   asking for help in finding a lost item
   asking for help in find a certain street, house, or store
   offering to give the child a toy or ice cream or candy
   offering to show the child a cute puppy or kitten
   inviting the child into the car to take him or her home (or to the zoo, etc.)

The idea is not to frighten the children, but to equip them to deal with a variety of situations. Teach students that after they say no, they should quickly leave and tell a trusted adult. As a memory device, consider teaching the slogan "No, Go, Tell."

3. Read a book on the topic of stranger education. Suggested titles: *Saying NO to Mr. Stranger* by Ginger Fulton, *The Berenstain Bears Learn About Strangers* by Stan and Jan Berenstain, *How Do You Know Who's a Stranger?* by M. Holland and J. Demers, *Who Is a Stranger and What Should I Do?* by Linda W. Girard, and *Strangers* by Dorothy Chlad.

4. **Closure:** "Remember, a stranger is anyone you don't know. Although most strangers are friendly and helpful, to be safe, never go for a ride or walk with a stranger. If a stranger asks you to go for a ride or walk, say no, quickly go away, and tell an adult."

LESSON 4: REPORTING EMERGENCIES

Preparation/Materials
- Student Activity page
- Cut out three construction paper circles, one red, one yellow, and one green for a visual.
- Telephones (if possible, real telephones)

Objectives
- Students will learn school fire drill procedures.
- Students will identify steps to take in case of fire.
- Students will practice reporting a fire or other emergency.

Background
These lessons on fire safety are adapted from *Learn Not to Burn,* a fire prevention and safety education curriculum produced by the United States National Fire Protection Agency. In this lesson students review school fire drill procedures and practice reporting a fire or other emergency.

• •

Lesson

1. Review your school fire drill procedures. Use the three circles to illustrate the three rules of a fire drill: Stop, listen, and go. Red means STOP whatever you're doing; yellow means wait or LISTEN instructions; green means GO out of the building.

2. Have a practice fire drill with your class.

3. Discuss what to do in case of fire in other than school settings. Use the Student Activity page in the Student Workbook of children reporting a fire, and have students identify what the children are doing. Stress that students should first get away from the fire and smoke and then quickly get adult help.

4. Teach students how to call for help if there is a fire or another emergency by dialing 911, 0 for operator, or your area's emergency number. Make a chant of the number for students to repeat, and prominently display the number in the classroom.

   Demonstrate dialing a telephone. Stress that if students report a fire, they shouldn't hang up until the operator tells them to. The operator will want to know where they are and what the problem is. Show the class where the phone number is written on a phone. (How to report emergencies is covered in more detail at the grade 1 level, but kindergartners should know how to dial the emergency number and tell where they are and what is happening.)

5. Put phones in a center for students to practice dialing and reporting.

6. **Closure**: "What do we do if there's a fire? (Elicit the main points covered in this lesson.) And we also learned how to use the telephone to report a fire or some other emergency."

• •

Related Activities

1. Ask a representative of the fire department to visit the class and discuss fire safety procedures. If the visit is scheduled as a culminating event, students can show what they have learned and be better prepared to ask questions.

2. Make firefighter props available at a center for dramatic play. Include toy firetrucks, a short piece of hose, a pair of boots, and a fire helmet.

3. Encourage the principal to have a fire drill shortly after you teach this lesson.

4. Review or teach student home addresses and telephone numbers. Ask each class member to draw a picture of his or her home. Then write each person's telephone number and address below the drawing. Students can take the drawings home and with parents' help memorize these basic facts.

LESSON 5: FIRE SAFETY—CRAWLING LOW

Preparation/Materials

- Pictures of smoke generated from various sources (a cookout, a cigarette or pipe, or coming out of chimney)
- Student Activity page
- Construction paper, one sheet per student
- Cotton balls, three or four per student
- Optional: sheet or blanket to use for practicing crawling low

Objectives

- Students will recognize that smoke can be just as dangerous as fire.
- Students will learn the crawl-low-in-smoke procedure.

Background

The United States National Fire Protection Agency (NFPA) urges that students learn the crawl-low-in-smoke procedure as a safety precaution because smoke is just as dangerous as fire. The agency explains: "Most casualties in fires are caused by smoke and toxic gases. Actually, flames and burns are responsible for the fewest number of deaths. More individuals are victims of asphyxiation, superheated air, and gases. . . . Thus, it is essential in moving through smoke in the evacuation of any building, including a home, to move rapidly in a crouching position below the visible smoke layer. If there is too much smoke to see the door, a person should crawl along the wall until the door is reached." Crawling close to the floor where the air and visibility are better greatly increases the chances of survival.

Lesson

1. Display the pictures of smoke coming from a variety of sources. Identify smoke as a smell that warns us. Teach the word *smoke* as new vocabulary. Note that usually we can stay away from smoke from a grill, campfire, or cigarette. Tell students that if there is a fire in a house or school, there will also be smoke, and because it's hard to breathe in smoke, smoke is dangerous.

2. Using the Student Activity page in the Student Workbook, show the children crawling low to stay out of the smoke. Point out that the bad air in the smoke rises and the good air stays below. So in case of fire, it's wise to crawl low on hands and knees to nearest exit. Stress that students should never try to "hide" from a fire, but should go to the nearest exit as quickly as possible.

3. Practice the crawling-low procedure with the class. Have students take turns holding a sheet about two feet above the floor. Ask students to crawl on their hands and knees underneath the sheet and go to the door.

4. **Student activity.** Use this NFPA suggestion for the follow-up activity. Have students paste cotton balls on the top of a piece of construction paper (to stand for smoke),

Then direct them to draw pictures of themselves crawling underneath. Write "Crawl low under smoke."

5. **Closure:** "Never try to hide from a fire. Get to the nearest way out as quickly as you can. If there is smoke, crawl low so that you can breathe the good air."

LESSON 6: STOP, DROP, AND ROLL

Preparation/Materials

- Mats for practicing stop, drop, and roll
- Book to read aloud about fire safety, including a warning about playing with matches
- Make the classroom train visual, car 7.
- Student Activities 1 & 2

Objectives

- Students will be aware that the "stop, drop, and roll" procedure can help to put out clothing fire and minimize injury.
- Students will practice the procedure.

Background

Learning the stop, drop, and roll technique can be important in saving lives and preventing serious burns. The National Fire Protection Agency claims that "many people have saved lives or averted serious burn injury" with the technique. In fact, NFPA says it "has documented cases where people have credited the 'Learn Not to Burn' public service announcements featuring Dick Van Dyke with helping to save their lives. Of these reported 'saves,' the majority have been due to the stop, drop, and roll technique and crawling-low-in-smoke technique."

Why does the stop, drop, and roll procedure work? "Rolling smothers the flames by removing oxygen. Covering the face with hands prevents the flames from burning your face and helps keep heat and smoke from reaching your lungs."

At the kindergarten level simply learning the basics of the technique is the goal. However, you should stress that although wrapping oneself in a rug, blanket, or large towel while rolling will help to smother the flames, only use these things if they are at hand. Don't go to get them.

• •

Lesson

1. Ask students to identify situations in which their clothing might catch on fire (for example, standing too close to a fire or being hit by sparks landing on clothing). Explain that in such a situation students must act quickly to put out the fire by using the stop, drop, and roll procedure.

2. Explain stop, drop, and roll. Stress the following points:
   - Stop: Don't run.
   - Drop: Drop to the ground (whether indoors or outdoors) and cover your face with your hands (to protect the face and keep smoke out of the lungs). Although wrapping oneself in a towel, blanket or rug helps to smother flames, don't run to get them.
   - Roll: Roll back and forth to put out the flames.

   Have students color Student Activity page 1 in the Student Workbook.

3. Practice how to stop, drop, and roll on mats. Have students call, "My clothes are on fire!" and then drop to smother the fire with the rolling technique.

4. Read *Matches, Lighters, and Firecrackers Are Not Toys* by Dorothy Chlad or a similar book that specifically warns about playing with matches.

5. **Student activity.** Complete car 7 in Student Activity 2 in the Student Workbook. Discuss each of the four danger items. Teach students that a red circle drawn around an object with a diagonal line drawn across means not to use or do something. Demonstrate on the board how to draw the symbol. After discussing each item, ask students to color the circle red and then draw a diagonal line through the object to complete the symbol.

   Add car 7 to the health train visual on display.

6. **Closure:** "If our clothing catches on fire, we should never run. We should stop, quickly drop to the ground, and roll back and forth to put out the fire. And we should learn not to burn by not playing with matches, candles, lighters, and outlets."

LESSON 7: APPROPRIATE AND INAPPROPRIATE TOUCHING

Preparation/Materials
- Student Activity page and/or Teacher Visual from Unit 2, Lesson 2
- For a discussion poster (step 4):
  Mount cut out pictures from magazines or coloring books of a doctor, nurse, and figures representing parents on the tagboard.
- Book to read aloud on topic of appropriate/inappropriate touch

Objectives
- Students will identify parts of the body that are private.
- Students will differentiate between appropriate and inappropriate touch.
- Students will practice saying no to inappropriate touch.
- Students will identify adults that can be a source of help.

Background
Some may question the need for child abuse education in Christian schools, but reliable research has shown that abuse does occur in Christian families and communities. And the rate of abuse is comparable to or only a little lower than that of the population as a whole. So although we may wish to believe that the problem does not exist in Christian communities, the facts do not support that view. Christian communities need to face the reality of abuse and help students develop skills for dealing with it.

Each level of the health education curriculum addresses the problem of sexual abuse. Since this is a sensitive subject, it is important for the school to contact parents or caregivers in advance and inform them of lesson content. You may wish to do this by letter or by meeting with parents. (Your school administrator may prefer to hold a meeting to which parents of all grades are invited. Some schools discuss the content of child abuse lessons at a parent orientation meeting during the first week of school.) Good communication with the home will give parents the opportunity to work with the school and to reinforce safety concepts.

The central focus of this lesson is safety, not sex education. In this unit students have been learning about safety. Now they are learning about one more type of safety—safety from sexual assault. Students who are aware of the danger of sexual abuse and know to protect themselves are less likely to become victims of sexual abuse.

To be effective, sexual abuse prevention education needs to cover the following basic areas in age-appropriate ways: (1) recognizing sexual abuse or differentiating between appropriate and inappropriate touch, (2) learning self-protection skills and techniques, and (3) identifying sources of help. We want to emphasize that presenting information on the subject of sexual abuse is not sufficient. Students also need to develop skills—decision-making skills and self-assertive protection skills. They must not only understand what inappropriate touch is, but must also understand what they can do about inappropriate touch.

It's also vital to present the material a nonthreatening way. Introduce the topic of touch in a way that makes you and the class feel comfortable. Having the classroom teacher present the material is preferable because an atmosphere of trust and rapport has already been established. If you are unable to teach the lesson comfortably, however, consider asking another qualified person to teach it, perhaps another teacher on the school staff. This is an important safety lesson, and it should be presented in a supportive environment.

As you teach the lesson, be clear and direct; use correct names when referring to body parts. If a child should begin to report abuse during class (an unlikely event), offer to talk with him or her later and consult with school staff.

· ·

Lesson

1. **Circle time.** Begin a discussion about different kinds of touches and how they make us feel. (For example: good touches such as handshakes and hugs, bad touches such as hitting and kicking, and confusing touches such as continuous tickling or touching certain parts of our bodies.

2. State that God made our bodies in such a way that we need every part. And every part is made in a good way. But some parts of our bodies are private. Teach the meaning of the word *private* as "hands off," or meaning that no one can touch the private parts of your body unless you say they can.

3. Discuss which parts of the body are private. With the aid of the Teacher Visual identify (review) the names for private body parts (buttocks, penis, vulva). If your school's policy is not to name body parts, use the visual of children in bathing suits to identify private parts of the body as the parts covered by a bathing suit. Tell students that when we're in public, we never wear less than a bathing suit because it covers private parts.

4. Using the discussion poster, talk about who can touch the body's private parts and in what circumstances. Have students identify the people pictured on the poster. Suggest situations in which others might need to touch private parts: doctors and nurses for a medical exam or other medical reason, parents to wash or take care of injury. Mention that babies need to be washed and diapered, but by school age children can wash private areas themselves.

5. Discuss what students should do if someone (even someone they know well) wants to touch the private parts of their body or asks students to touch them in their private parts. They can say no, quickly leave, and tell an adult about what happened—even if the the person tells them to keep it a secret. Together practice saying no assertively. Then with students identify some adults that they could tell.

6. Read an appropriate book with the class about appropriate/inappropriate touches. Suggestions: *Private Zone* by Frances S. Dayee, *It's My Body* by Lory Freeman, *It's Okay to Say No* by Amy Bahr, or *My Body Is Private* by Linda W. Girard.

7. **Closure:** "Today we learned that God made all the parts of the body. They are all important and good. Some parts are private. And we learned what to do if we don't want someone to touch our private parts: say no, go away, and tell someone else about it."

Related Activities

- Enjoy good touches with the class by playing hug tag. Play the game in a gym or other large space. Accompany the game with music. Start with students moving around in random order to the music. When the music stops, each child should hug another. Then have the groups of two move to the music and at the next pause hug another group of two. The game continues until the class becomes one group. Use the game to talk about good touches. Give students the opportunity to talk about touches they enjoy.

Unit 7

Preventing Health Problems

Goals

- Students will develop an awareness of potential health and safety problems.
- Students will understand how individuals choices can contribute to health.

Background

This unit continues to raise consciousness about health and safety issues and to promote awareness of the important health choices students make daily. The unit also introduces the topic of substance abuse and lays the foundation for lessons at higher levels. We are all aware that substance abuse is a serious problem in North American society, and *Horizons Health* addresses the problem at each grade level. At the kindergarten level, students begin with basics, distinguishing safe from unsafe substances, learning what medicine is for and how to take it safely. They identify smoke in the environment and smoking, in particular, as detrimental to the health of their lungs, and they are encouraged to stay "smoke free."

AIDS—acquired immune deficiency syndrome—is not specifically addressed in kindergarten. However, concepts essential to understanding AIDS are introduced. Students learn about communicable disease and one way germs are spread (droplet infection) and about wellness behaviors to reduce risk of infection. Lessons in higher grades build on this information so that students receive AIDS education in developmentally appropriate ways.

Nonetheless, because AIDS receives wide attention in the media, even very young children may be aware of AIDS and raise questions about it. Teachers must be prepared to answer their questions with age-appropriate information. The United States Department of Health and Human Services' Guidelines for Effective School Health Education to Prevent the Spread of Aids (MMWR Supplement, January 29, 1988) suggests that education about AIDS for students in early elementary grades should center on allaying excessive fears and consist of these three concepts:

- AIDS is a disease that is causing some adults to get very sick, but it does not commonly affect children.
- AIDS is very hard to get. You cannot get it just by being near or touching someone who has it.
- Scientists all over the world are working hard to find a way to stop people from getting AIDS and to cure those who have it.

Vocabulary

Integrate the following suggested vocabulary:

germs	lungs	air
sick	poison	cigarettes
smoke	medicine	breathe

Lesson Resources

Lesson 1

Aliki. *Manners.* New York: Greenwillow, 1990.

    One page, "Look at Daniel," graphically illustrates the need for using tissues or hankies.

Berenstain, Stan and Jan. *The Berenstain Bears Go to the Doctor.* New York: Random, 1981.

Berger, Melvin. *Germs Make Me Sick.* New York: Crowell, 1985.

Brandenberg, Fritz. *I Wish I Was Sick, Too.* New York: Greenwillow, 1976.

Rey, Margaret. *Curious George Goes to the Hospital.* Boston: Houghton Mifflin, 1973.

Rockwell, Anne and Harlow. *Sick in Bed.* New York: Macmillan, 1982.

Vincent, Gabrielle. *Feel Better, Ernest.* New York: Greenwillow, 1988.

Lesson 2

Drugs Can Be Dangerous. Filmstrip/cassette. QED Products.

    Teaches students about the danger of taking medications not prescribed to them or not given them by their adult caregiver.

Drugs, Poisons and Little Children. Filmstrip/cassette. Educational Activities.

    Reinforces the concept that sniffing, tasting, or ingesting any unknown substance can be deadly.

Lesson 3

Starting Free: Good Air for Me. American Cancer Society, 1987.

    This preschool smoking-prevention package contains a poster, five story booklets, plastic hand puppets, coloring book, stickers, and home activity sheets. Available from local chapters free of charge.

Lungs Are for Life—K. Kit. American Lung Association, 1983.

    The kit includes a teacher guide, activity sheets, and a colorful poster. Sections 3 and 4 relate to Lesson 3 of this unit. Contact a local branch of the American Lung Association to obtain the materials.

No Smoking: A Coloring and Activities Book. South Deerfield, Mass.

    Activities and illustrations emphasize good reasons not to smoke and explain the bad effects of smoking. Order from the publisher: 200 State Rd., South Deerfield, Massachusetts 01373-0200; phone 800-628-7733.

Octopuff in Kumquat. Film. American Lung Association, 1983.

    This nine-minute film about an octopus who works to clean up air pollution can be purchased or borrowed from the American Lung Association.

Lesson 4

Chlad, Dorothy. *Poisons Make You Sick.* Chicago: Childrens Press, 1984.

Skidmore, Steve. *Poison! Beware! Be an Expert Poison Spotter.* Brookfield, Conn.: Millbrook Press, 1991.

    Although this is intended for students in grades 2-6, teachers may find this a helpful resource.

Poison Control Center. Contact local poison control centers for educational materials and take-home handouts.

Lesson 5

An Early Start to Good Health. Kit. American Cancer Society.

One section of this kit, "My Body," is intended for use at the kindergarten level. It contains a filmstrip and accompanying cassette of a "mini-musical" story, a teacher guide (with suggestions for activities and a playscript, music, and suggestions for classroom performance, five blackline masters, and a colorful poster. An excellent resource for a rousing culminating lesson.) Contact the local chapter of The Cancer Society to obtain a hit.

LESSON 1: SICK DAYS

Preparation/Materials
- Chart paper
- Student Activity page
- Tissues cut into 2"-3" pieces, one piece per student
- Squirt gun and colored liquid

Objectives
- Students will describe how they feel when they are sick.
- Students will identify germs as a cause of illness.
- Students will identify ways to prevent the spread of sickness.

Background
Children at this age are prone to upper respiratory diseases such as colds, sinusitis, and influenza. They may be more susceptible because their body's immune response is not fully developed. Because they are vulnerable to these diseases, it is very important to teach and practice ways to avoid spreading germs. Bear in mind that the setup of a typical elementary school classroom is conducive for spreading communicable diseases. Children usually sit close together in rows or in a circle, and if they sneeze or cough without covering their mouth and nose, they can easily infect classmates. So throughout the school year reinforce the concepts of this lesson through practical application, through washing hands and enforcing the "cover your mouth and nose when sneezing and coughing" rule.

• •

Lesson

1. Elicit from students descriptions of how they feel when they are sick. Note that no matter how much good food we eat and how much we exercise, sometimes we do get sick.

2. Enjoy the following poem with the class.

   Sick Days
   On days when I am sick in bed
   My mother is so nice;
   She brings me bowls of chicken soup
   And ginger ale with ice.

   She cuts the crusts off buttered toast
   And serves it on a tray
   And sits down while I eat it
   And doesn't go away.

   She reads my favorite books to me;
   She lets me take my pick;
   And everything is perfect—
   Except that I am sick!

   Mary Ann Hoberman

Discuss the poem together. How does the child in the poem feel about being sick? Elicit from students their feelings about being sick. What kinds of things have others done for them to cheer them up? What kinds of things can they do to support others who are sick? (Include the idea that showing concern for the sick is one way of loving our neighbor.)

Ask: "What do we do when we're sick to help us get better?" (Stay in bed and rest, see a doctor, take medicine, and sometimes eat special food.)

3. Explain that many sicknesses are caused by germs. Germs are so small we can't see them with our eyes alone, but when they are inside us they can make us sick. Germs get inside us in various ways, and we can spread them to others.

   Work with the class to develop a chart of ways to keep germs from spreading. Make sketches to illustrate each point.

   Include the following ideas:
   - Stay home and get extra rest.
   - Cover your mouth when you cough or sneeze and throw away used tissues.
   - Use a squirt gun and colored liquid to show how coughing and sneezing can spread germs.
   - Use your own personal health items—drinking cup, toothbrush, washcloth, and towel.
   - Wash your hands often (always before eating and after using the toilet).
   - Get shots to prevent certain diseases.

   As you go over the completed chart, recall the connection between loving our neighbors and obeying rules (Unit 6, Lesson 1). How will following the health rules on the chart show love for neighbor?

4. **Student activity.** Refer to the activity page in the Student Workbook. Direct students to cut out the arm of the boy and tape or glue it to the figure of the boy. The hand should cover the boy's mouth. Then give each child a piece of tissue to glue or tape to the designated area on the figure of the girl. Review why covering the mouth and nose with tissue when we cough or sneeze helps to keep germs and sickness from spreading.

5. **Closure:** "Today we talked about being sick. We talked about how we feel when we're sick, about what others do to help us, and about what we can do for others. There are several ways we can keep sickness from spreading." (Elicit from students items listed in step 3.)

Related Activities

1. Center idea: have props available for playing sick child/well child.

2. Read a book such as *Sick in Bed* by Anne and Harlow Rockwell, *I Wish I Was Sick, Too* by Franz Brandenberg, *The Berenstain Bears Go to the Doctor* by Stan and Jan Berenstain, or *Feel Better, Ernest* by Gabrielle Vincent. Or show students the amusing pictures in Aliki's book *Manners* about coughing, sneezing, and runny noses to reinforce the idea of using tissues or hankies. *Germs Make Me Sick* by Melvin Berger is somewhat advanced but is helpful in explaining what causes sickness.

3. Read a book such as *Curious George Goes to the Hospital* by Margaret Rey. Ask students how they would feel if a friend were in the hospital. What could they do to show their love and concern?

4. Visit a hospital or nursing home and sing songs for the patients.

LESSON 2: TAKING YOUR MEDICINE

Preparation/Materials
- Student Activity pages 1–5
- Complete car 8 of the classroom health train by gluing enlarged pictures of health friends on the sheet of construction paper. Add the words "Get to know these health helpers."
- Optional: flannelgraph
- Optional: puppets or other manipulatives for presenting "What If?" situations

Objectives
- Students will recognize the importance of taking medicines safely.
- Students will generate safe responses to specific situations of risk.
- Students will identify community health-care helpers.

Background
The purpose of this lesson is to stress one basic safety rule: only take medicine from a parent or other adult caregiver. Although the rule is simple, enough children ignore the rule each year to warrant a separate lesson about it. Children are naturally curious, and unknown substances—especially those that look like candy—have great attraction.

Lesson
1. Refer to Student Activity pages 1–5 in the Student Workbook to discuss the use of medicines.
   - Student Activity 1. Have students identify what the scene shows (a "child" is sick and the doctor is prescribing medicine to help make him/her better). Tell students that medicines are prescribed by doctors to help us get well when we are sick.
   - Student Activity 2. Ask: "Who gives children medicine?" (Only parents or other adults responsible for them.)
   - Student Activity 3. Have students identify what the problem is. (The child took the medicine on his own.) Repeat the rule: students should never take medicines on their own. Taking medicines on their own could make them very sick. They might take something that's bad for them or take too much of something. Because medicines are strong, it's important to take just the right amount. Clearly make the point that even though some medicines may look like candy, they are not, and taking them could be dangerous.
   - Student Activity 4.: Stress that if children don't feel well they should tell an adult. If they're sick, they need to rest in bed. Sometimes they may need medicine to help them get better. Ask: "Who should give you medicine?" (Adults only.)

   If time allows, have the students color the Student Activity pages.

2. Tell "What If?" stories. Consider using puppets or other manipulatives to act out the situations. Suggested situations:
   - "What if you find a bottle while you're playing in a friend's garage? You open the bottle and find some pink pills that look good. What should you do?"
   - "What if your friend finds some pills on the counter in the bathroom and wants you to try them—just to see if they taste good?"
   - "What if you see a bottle of cough syrup on the dresser and remember that when you were sick, your father or mother gave you some when you were coughing? It tasted pretty good. You'd like to drink some more from the bottle. Should you open the bottle and drink it? What should you do?"

3. **Student activity.** Refer to Student Activity 5 in the Student Workbook. Have students identify the health helpers pictured. What does each do? How does each help us to stay healthy? Who gives us medicine? Students can color the pictures to complete another car for their health trains.

   Add car 8 to the classroom health train.

4. **Closure:** "Medicine is something we can take when we're sick to help us get better or to help us feel better. But it's important to take just the right medicine and just the right amount of medicine. Too much could make us sicker. So we never take medicine on our own; we only take medicine that a health helper or our parents give us."

● ●

Related Activities

1. Invite a pharmacist, doctor, or nurse to the class to discuss their roles in providing drugs and medicines to children.

2. Show a filmstrip on the lesson topic. Two suggestions are *Drugs Can Be Dangerous* and *Drugs, Poisons, and Little Children.*

3. Collect "tools" (or pictures of tools) commonly used by health professionals and discuss what each item is used for. Include a stethoscope, otoscope, tongue depressors, and cotton swabs.

LESSON 3: BE SMOKE FREE

Preparation/Materials
- Student Activities 1 & 2
- Pictures of smoke sources used in Unit 6, Lesson 5
- Piece of construction paper, one per student

Objectives
- Students will identify negative effects of smoke on the body.
- Students will know how smoke enters the body.
- Students will desire to be smoke free.

Background
You may question whether including a lesson on the topic of smoking is appropriate at the kindergarten level. However, the American Cancer Society notes that children form opinions about smoking at a very young age. And they report that 41 percent of preschoolers questioned in one study had actually tried cigarettes. Dealing with the subject of smoking when children are impressionable will help set them in the right direction and form attitudes that will influence them to decide not to smoke.

Many excellent materials for this lesson are available from both the American and Canadian Cancer Society. At present free kits are available upon request for preschool-K. The American Cancer Society kit is called *Starting Free: Good Air for Me.* Contact your local society well ahead of teaching this lesson to obtain the kits. Other organizations to contact for lesson-related materials are the Canadian Lung Association and the American Lung Association.

• •

Lesson

1. Begin by having students breathe in and out. Teach the word *breathe.* Explain that we breathe all the time and that we began to breathe as soon as we were born.

2. Refer to Student Activity 1 in the Student Workbook to give a simple explanation of breathing: air comes into our lungs when we breathe in and goes out when we breathe out.

3. Brainstorm some sources of smoke. Use the pictures collected for Unit 6, Lesson 5, or draw simple pictures on the board to illustrate as students make suggestions (include factories, campfires, cigarettes, and pipes or cigars. Ask students how breathing smoke makes them feel (or describe how it makes you feel). Explain that smoky air is not good air to breathe. Use the visual to show how smoke gets into our lungs as we breathe.

   Note that smoking is an unhealthy choice and that both the smoker and those near the smoker are affected by the habit.

4. Make up a chant encouraging students to stay away from smoky places and from smoking when they get older. (Discuss the growing number of smoke-free areas in public places in North America.) Consider chanting the Cancer Society's slogan "Let's Be Smoke Free."

5. **Student activity.** Refer to Student Activity 2 in the Student Workbook to teach the non-smoking symbol. Then direct students to cut apart the puzzle strips and put them together correctly to form a picture. What symbol do they find on the t-shirt? Provide the children with construction paper on which they can glue their picture-puzzles.

6. **Closure:** "Today we talked about why we should be smoke free. We learned that our lungs stay healthier if we don't breathe in smoke."

● ●

Related Activities

1. Show *Octopuff in Kumquat,* an American Lung Association film.

2. Use material available from national cancer organizations or lung associations for follow-up or center activities.

LESSON 4: THAT'S POISON!

Preparation/Materials

- Student Activity pages 1 & 2
- Pictures cut from magazines or newspapers of a variety of household products that are poisonous/not safe to taste and of foods that are safe to eat or taste (see step 3 for suggestions). Consider mounting the pictures on cards or heavy paper.
- Construct car 9 of the health train by gluing enlarged symbols on construction paper. Color the circles red and draw diagonal lines through them to complete the negative symbol. Add the words "Learn to say NO to."

- Optional: a container (empty and clean) with the poison sign

Objectives

- Students will identify the symbol for poisons.
- Students will know that tasting unknown substances is dangerous.
- Students will identify some common substances that are poisonous.

• •

Lesson

1. **Discussion.** Have students look at their skull and crossbones visual—Student Activity 1 in the Student Workbook. Explain what the sign means: poison—keep away. Teach the word *poison* as new vocabulary. Ask if students have ever seen the sign and if so, where. If possible, show students a clean container with the sign.

   Explain that even though a container does not have a warning sign on it, the substance may be poison. Teach the basic rule: never taste or swallow an unknown substance. To prevent possible poisoning, always "ask before tasting." If students can't find someone to ask, wait—don't taste.

2. Use pictures of various products and foods to help students differentiate safe/unsafe substances. Ask students by turns to choose a picture and identify what it's used for and whether or not it's something that can safely be eaten. Or give every two students a picture and have them decide together the object's purpose and safety.

   Suggested pictures to include:
   cigarettes
   car care products
   cleansers
   furniture polish
   insect repellent
   rodent poison
   nail polish and remover
   oven cleaner

mothballs
bug killers
bleach and other laundry products
food items

3. **Student activity.** Use Student Activity 2 to review safety concepts. After working with the class to identify the meaning of each picture/symbol, give class members an opportunity to color the circle and the diagonal strip across the picture red.

Place car 9 on the classroom health train.

4. **Closure:** "We learned the sign for poison today (refer to sign), and we learned this important safety rule: always ask before tasting anything that may not be food. If there's no one to ask, wait—don't taste!"

● ●

Related Activities

1. Contact the local poison control center for materials for students to take home. Some centers have stickers for students stick on household poisons, or brochures with lists of common household poisons with suggestions for proper storing.

2. Working as a class, cut out magazine pictures and create two collages—one of things good to eat and one of things that are harmful to eat.

3. Read *Poisons Make You Sick* by Dorothy Chlad or stories and booklets available from the local poison control center.

LESSON 5: CULMINATING HEALTH LESSON

Preparation/Materials
- For completing student train booklets: Student Activity page
  parent letter to include with the health train, one copy per student
- Make the caboose for the classroom train visual.
- Optional: plan for nutritious snacks to be served (have students each bring in one thing).
- Optional: caboose wheels:
  black construction paper wheels, four per student
  paper fasteners, four per student

Objectives
- Students will review good health practices.
- Students will choose to follow good health practices.

Lesson

1. Begin with a small group activity. Divide the class into groups and assign or let each group choose one health practice to pantomime. After each pantomime, have the rest of the class identify what they're acting out. Some health practices to pantomime: brushing teeth, washing hands, exercising, sleeping, following safety rules for crossing the street, and covering a cough or sneeze.

2. **Student activity.** Refer to the activity page in the Student Workbook. Help students complete their health train booklets and add the caboose to the train on display. Students should color the caboose—the back cover. If the inside of the cover is blank, ask students to draw a picture of themselves doing something healthy. And if the student booklets have black construction paper wheels, help students cut out and mount the wheels with paper fasteners.

   Assemble the health train booklets. (Give students a copy of the explanatory letter to parents to take home with the booklet.)

3. Use the completed health train to review health concepts. Consider ending the train project the same way it started—with a student train chugging around the class and a chant urging everyone to get on board.

4. Sing songs the class learned during the health program. Include songs thanking God for health and for food.

5. Optional: Close with a feast of nutritious snacks.

Related Activities

- Have students plan and present a program about ways to stay healthy. (Use materials from the kit *An Early Start to Good Health.*) Invite parents to attend or give the program for grade 1 students.

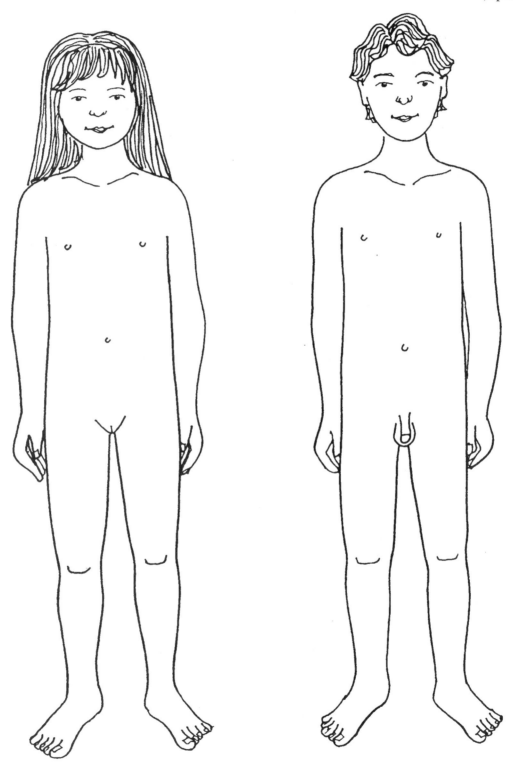

Permission granted to reproduce this page only.

Permission granted to reproduce this page only.

Dear Parents,

We have been studying health, using the *Horizons Health* curriculum published by Alpha Omega Publications, Inc. One of the projects we have worked on is a health train. As you look at this booklet with your child, you might want to emphasize the following ideas.

Car 1: It's important to dress right for the weather.

Car 2: Exercise and fitness are important. What are some different ways to exercise?
Do you have any "family exercises"?

Car 3: Getting enough rest is essential. Talk about the reasons for having a set bedtime.

Car 4: Food is fuel to give us energy and help us to grow. Perhaps at a meal explain how certain foods build strong bodies.

Car 5: In order to stay healthy it is important to keep clean. Besides it feels good to keep clean! Clean teeth are important, too. Not eating too much sugar also helps to keep teeth healthy.

Car 6: Students should practice safety when going to and from school. Discuss family rules about strangers. Rules are for our own safety and happiness but also for the wellbeing of others.

Car 7: Review these safety concepts:
- Do not play with matches, candles, lighters, electrical outlets.
- If clothes are burning, stop, drop, and roll to put out the fire.
- Dial _____ in an emergency.
- Don't hide from a fire. Get out quickly. If there's lots of smoke, crawl low.

You make wish to have a family fire drill.

Car 8: Doctors, dentists, and other health care workers are friends. They help us to prevent and to recover from diseases. They care for injuries. Children can be health helpers by washing hands and by covering their mouth when coughing or sneezing.

Car 9: Hold a matter-of-fact discussion of the symbols. Try not to upset the children by being overly dramatic. The symbols stand for poisons (household cleaners, etc), medicines or pills, cigarettes, matches, and lighters, strangers, and "unknowns." Unknowns are plants or substances not meant to be eaten or swallowed.